For Esker

with deep gratitude
and much love
from
          Lilian
Chapel Hill, April 2008

Before Freud

Before Freud

Hysteria and Hypnosis
in Later Nineteenth-Century
Psychiatric Cases

Lilian R. Furst

Lewisburg
Bucknell University Press

Associated University Presses
2010 Eastpark Boulevard
Cranbury, NJ 08512

The paper used in this publication meets the requirements of the American National Standard for Permanence of Paper for Printed Library Materials Z39.48-1984.

Library of Congress Cataloging-in-Publication Data

Furst, Lilian R.
    Before Freud : hysteria and hypnosis in later nineteenth-century psychiatric cases / Lilian R. Furst.
        p. cm.
    Includes bibliographical references.
    ISBN 978-0-8387-5698-0 (alk. paper)
        1. Psychiatry—History—19th century—Sources.   2. Hysteria—History—19th century—Sources.   3. Hypnosis—History—19th century—Sources.   4. Psychiatry—Case studies.   5. Hysteria—Case studies.   6. Hypnosis—Case studies.   I. Title.
    [DNLM: 1. Hysteria—history. 2. History, 19th Century. 3. Hypnosis—history.   WM 11.1 F991b 2008]
    RC438.F87 2008
    616.89—dc22

                                                                                                2007033203

To C. Frederick Irons III, MD
whose kindness and empathy are far beyond mere words of praise

Contents

Preface

Mention the psychiatric case history toward the end of the nineteenth century and thoughts will automatically turn to Freud. And rightly so, for his *Studien über Hysterie* (1896; *Studies on Hysteria*) inaugurated an entirely new, perhaps it might even be called a revolutionary turn in the history of psychiatry with the crystallization of psychoanalysis, a method that rapidly became—and remained—at once popular and controversial. His *Bruchstück einer Hysterie-Analyse* (1905; *Fragment of an Analysis of a Case of Hysteria*), commonly known as *Dora,* is still widely read and disputed, especially since the advent of feminist criticism. *Dora* was followed by *Bemerkungen über einen Fall von Zwangsneurose* (1909; *The Ratman*) and *Geschichte einer infantilen Neurose* (1914; *The Wolfman*). These case histories, though classics of Western thought, are read as in a vacuum, as if they had sprung from nowhere, free-standing, as it were, devoid of a historical context other than that of the Viennese culture of Freud's time.

In order fully to understand Freud's significance in the evolution of psychiatry we need to ask, Who were his predecessors in the writing of case histories? What were their characteristics? In what respects did Freud follow on or depart from them? It is particularly important to pose these questions because, as Micale has recently pointed out: "The period 1870–1910 witnessed an unprecedented burst of creative psychological theorizing in Europe and the United States. This was the founding generation of modern psychology, psychiatry, and psychotherapy, during which the sciences of the mind largely assumed the theoretical and professional forms in which we know them today."[1] This crucial period, as well as earlier phases in the history of psychiatry, have in the past thirty or so years been amply chronicled (by such scholars as Bynum, Ellenberger, Micale, Oppenheim, Scull, and Shorter, to name just a few). Yet these works offer readers a mediated, of necessity interpreted view, whereas to read the actual case histories allows a firsthand knowledge.

Concentrating on the period 1869–94, that is, about the quarter of a century before Freud came onto the scene, this volume aims to present some of the case histories of the time. A case history has been defined as an organized set of facts relevant to the development of an individual or group condition under study or treatment, especially in sociology, psychiatry, or medicine. All the case histories collected here were written by physicians recording their own cases. Yet, though interesting, at times indeed exciting, none has—or ever had—the kind of readership Freud still enjoys today,

One reason for the relative neglect of these later nineteenth-century case histories is their comparative inaccessibility for an English-speaking audience in the early twenty-first century. I have deliberately chosen case histories of intrinsic and/or historical significance that have for various reasons remained beyond the reach of today's readers, most often because they have not hitherto been translated into English. Admittedly, the American George M. Beard did write his seminal article launching the concept of neurasthenia in English, but it was published in the *Boston Medical and Surgical Journal* of 1869 and so is not readily available except in a few specialized libraries of medical history. The other physicians represented in this collection wrote in German or French and have either never been translated or not recently enough to be readily found. For instance, Richard von Krafft-Ebing's *Psychopathia Sexualis* (1886), last translated into English in 1926, now has more notoriety than readers. Arthur Schnitzler's study of six cases of functional aphonia (1889) has hardly been current even in German until it was retrieved from the Austrian medical journal in which it originally appeared and reprinted in the 1988 volume of his *Medizinische Schriften* (Medical Writings). On the other hand, I have omitted Hippolyte Bernheim, certainly a crucial figure who published numerous case histories, since all his major works have been translated (see introduction and bibliography). The situation of Jean-Martin Charcot is considerably more complicated. There is no complete translation of his main work, the *Leçons du mardi à la Salpêtrière;* nine excerpts from it appeared in 1987, concerned primarily with unusual neurological instances ("Parkinson's Disease: A Case without Tremor") or with problems of differential diagnosis ("Syphilis, Locomotor Ataxia, Facial Paralysis: Three Diseases and Their Relationships"). His fascinating, exciting psychiatric case histories, included here, have been reprinted in French but not translated. The situation of Pierre Janet is both simpler and sadder. While his principal book, *L'État mental des hystériques,* was translated as *The*

Mental State of Hysterics just eight years after its publication in France in 1893, most of his highly detailed, insightful case histories either appeared in such journals as the *Revue de médecine* (1887–88) and the *Archives de Neurologie* (1891 and 1892) or are more or less hidden away in the *Revue philosophique* of the late 1880s and early 1890s. These case histories, in many respects the most direct predecessors to Freud, have never been reprinted in French, let alone translated into English. This volume is, therefore, in a sense, a kind of rescue operation.

My choice has also been determined by what seemed most significant at that time as well as in the historical perspective. Thus, Beard's concept of neurasthenia, which at best comes across nowadays as quaint and unscientific, at worst as verging on self-promotion inspired by financial motives, was accepted throughout the later nineteenth and well into the twentieth century as a legitimate, widespread diagnosis of an amorphous "nervous" illness. Krafft-Ebing's findings on sexual aberrations aroused furor as being absolutely scandalous, so scandalous that sales of his book were restricted to medical and legal professionals. Schnitzler, whose reputation now rests squarely on his literary works, wielded influence as the editor of the *Internationale klinische Rundschau* (International clinical review), which published reviews of new medical works and was therefore instrumental in the diffusion of innovative theories and practices.

Each selection is introduced by a headnote designed to provide some personal and professional information about the author, and to comment on the central concepts expounded in the piece as well as on the manner in which they are put forward, for the way in which these case histories were recorded varies enormously and proves more important than might be assumed. Beard's front of self-assurance and Charcot's grandiose flamboyance are in stark contrast to Schnitzler's circumspection and Janet's modesty. While it would be an overstatement to claim a direct correlation between the mode of presentation and the level of acceptance accorded to the actual ideas, the literary/rhetorical force turns out to play a role that is by no means negligible and that must be heeded.

The introduction cannot possibly aspire to offer an overview of the currents and countercurrents, the hypotheses and heresies that made up psychiatry in the late nineteenth century. At most it seeks to identify the common prevailing beliefs shared by these figures together with the divergences of emphasis and stance among them. Many questions have to be addressed: What kind of patients did they see? How did they envisage the etiology of "nervous" afflictions? What hopes did they hold for remediation, and what methods did they regard as potentially effective? From the answers to such inquiries it fairly quickly becomes apparent that even where there is a show of self-confidence, much of late nineteenth-century psychiatry still consisted to a greater or lesser extent of groping explorations of a predominantly dark area.

It is only by seeing Freud against this background that we can begin truly to appreciate the extent of his originality not just in his devising of psychoanalysis but above all in his grasp of the profound importance of the unconscious in the motivation of behavior. Some of his predecessors had a limited intuition of this; however, his insights into the hidden workings of the human mind represent a gigantic leap forward.

NOTE

1. Mark S. Mecale and Paul Lerner, eds. *Traumatic Pasts: History, Psychiatry, and Trauma in the Modern Age* (Cambridge: Cambridge University Press, 2001), 118.

Acknowledgments

IT GIVES ME GREAT PLEASURE TO RECORD MY GRATITUDE TO THOSE WHO have furthered this project:

The members of the Psychoanalytic Theory Reading Group at the University of North Carolina, who have over many years fostered my interest in Freud and the history of psychiatry and who have discussed some sections of this book.

Sarah K. Cantrell, my ever willing research assistant, who has generously helped me in so many ways beyond the call of duty.

David Freeman, MD, who provided me with marketing information.

Steve and Madeline Levine, dear friends, who offered support and suggestions, especially at a time of discouragement.

Thomas Nixon, reference librarian at Davis Library, University of North Carolina, who unearthed the French cases from various journals of the period and kindly made copies for me.

Ester Zago, my first PhD in the United States, who has become my intellectual sister and who so gladly undertook the task of proofreading

Before Freud

Introduction:
Demons, Lesions, and Neuroses

IN THE HIERARCHY OF MEDICAL SPECIALTIES THAT EMERGED DURING the nineteenth century, psychiatry occupied a lowly position. Compared to the momentous advances made, for example, by bacteriology in the formulation of germ theory and by surgery in the discovery of anesthesia, antisepsis, and asepsis, psychiatry had little or nothing of equal import to show. The rapid and definitive progress of somatic medicine pulled far ahead of the much slower, halting developments in mental medicine. But to regard nineteenth-century psychiatry with a condescension amounting to contempt is a grave error, for significant changes did take place. However—and this is one of nineteenth-century psychiatry's difficulties—they were not amenable to scientific proof as the phenomena observable under the microscope or in the test tube were. Some of the hypotheses put forward gained credence and were fashionable for a while, only to be discredited and abandoned later. The history of psychiatry in the nineteenth century is by no means a linear march forward; it is much rather a journey, a quest full of astonishing twists and turns, misconceptions and insights, that cumulatively do advance the field through greater understanding of the perplexing manifestations of mental disorders.

The magnitude of the advances made can best be assessed by comparison not with contemporaneous bacteriology or surgery but with the practices of psychiatry in the previous century. Even the term *psychiatrist* is misplaced since it was imported from the German *psychiater* late in the nineteenth century, replacing *alienist* as the word to describe one who handles the mentally disturbed. *Alienist* in turn was a more polite and respectful successor to the eighteenth-century *mad-doctor*, whose function was in effect hardly more than custodial, and who was a "punitive persona,"[1] charged with the control of "luna-

ticks," as they were then called, locked into "madhouses." In today's
parlance we would say that they were warehoused as unfortunate, but
also threatening creatures who had to be sequestered for the protection of society at large. Lunatics were feared, even when they were
actually harmless, because they were thought to be possessed by
demons, avatars of the devil. So irrational fears and superstitions with
a vaguely religious coloring dogged those who suffered from mental
illnesses. Yet at the same time, they were, paradoxically, a source of
fascination for the curious who were willing to pay a small fee in order
to stare at their antics on open days at Bedlam.

The madhouses, such as Bedlam, were primarily repositories for
lunatics, which aimed above all to remove them from the public arena.
Since they were regarded as incurable, no attempt was made to try to
remediate their condition in any way. The earliest effort at some form
of treatment occurred at the York Retreat, founded in 1813 by the
Quaker tea merchant Samuel Tuke, who introduced a regimen of
exercise, work, and amusements in the belief that such a humane
approach would help disturbed minds to return to normal or at least
to their optimal level. In 1817 an American counterpart, "The Asylum for the Relief of Friends Deprived of Their Reason," opened in
Frankford near Philadelphia. The word *asylum*, with its connotations
of shelter, is an important indicator of the new attitude that hoped to
transform inmates into orderly people by treating them as though
they were sane, or at least as human beings, not as dangerous animals
to be chained and curbed by various sinister devices, as they often
were in the madhouses. Decent beds, proper food, patience, kindness, cheerfulness, and organized activities were the visible expressions of Tuke's model of "moral treatment," but even more crucial
was the underlying faith in the possibility of restoring the lunatic to
a better state. However, these initiatives stemmed from compassion,
not from medical knowledge.

The dearth not only of medical knowledge but even of interest in
the mentally disturbed helps to account for the puzzling absence of
psychiatric case histories in the earlier periods. As that most meticulous scholar Dorrit Cohn laments: "I have not been able to find any
specialized work that probes the historical evolution of the case history as a genre."[2] Although the eminent physician Sir Thomas Sydenham had in the seventeenth century already kept careful observations on the vicissitudes of physical maladies, no parallel records were
thought to be worth maintaining for mental illnesses because lunacy
was regarded as beyond remedy. Moreover, humoral medicine, the

dominant theory from Galen right up to the nineteenth century, envisaged patients as fitting into four distinctive constitutional types, to be treated according to age, temperament, time of year, climate, and so forth, not as individuals with particularized histories. Also, there were no forums or journals for the dissemination of information. *The Lancet,* founded by Thomas Wakely in 1825, was originally intended to serve the political purpose of improving the status and conditions of the medical profession, not to publish reports of cases or discoveries.

The crystallization of the psychiatric case history into its nineteenth-century forms could take place only after a radical modification had taken place in the conceptualization of the patient. Apart from "lunatics," whose contact with reality was severely ruptured, other labels were introduced: the "half-mads" (*demi-fous*) and the "alienated" (*aliénés*), as they were called in France, or in Germany the *nervenkrank* (suffering from nervous diseases) in contrast to those who were *geisteskrank* (insane). The idea of a graduated continuum between madness and sanity began to be recognized, corresponding roughly to the modern categories of psychotic and neurotic. The half-mads and the alienated were so much less disturbed that they could continue to function, albeit with some impairment. Such patients were "claimed as the legitimate objects of psychiatric knowledge and solicitude."[3] They offered welcome opportunities for clinical observation and research because they were generally far more responsive than lunatics who had withdrawn into their bizarre private worlds. They were medically attractive, so to speak, since they were deemed capable of improvement under favorable circumstances. What exactly these circumstances were, that is, the most effective modes of treatment, was a matter of much debate. The ideal opportunity for airing the divergent methods favored by various doctors was the case history with its record of symptoms, treatment, and outcome.

The treatments extended to the half-mads were closely related to their social class and their financial capacity. The indigent, the poor in working-class occupations had no choice but to go to the free public institutions such as La Salpêtrière in Paris. Charcot's patients there at the Tuesday morning walk-in clinic near the hospital entrance were almost without exception lower class with just a sprinkling of petite bourgeoisie. This also holds true of the women who consulted Schnitzler at Vienna's Policlinic, and of Janet's patients. Only Krafft-Ebing's sexual deviants spanned the class divides, comprising the well-to-do and a few minor aristocrats alongside workers.

But this was not the rule. Generally, the middle and upper classes, who obviously also had their share of lunatics, handled the problem differently. Through much of the nineteenth century still, those who could afford it would make secret arrangements to hide the mentally sick in their families to avoid the disgrace emanating from such persons. Mrs. Rochester, the madwoman in the attic in Charlotte Brontë's *Jane Eyre* (1847), is guarded by a servant dedicated exclusively to that task. Similarly, the young doctor in Arthur Conan Doyle's *The Stark Munro Letters* (1895) is employed to secure a lord's deranged son in his castle. Private madhouses, managed by clergy, were also established, first in London in the seventeenth century, spreading elsewhere in the eighteenth, and known euphemistically in France as *maisons de santé* (health houses!).

Thus a two-tier system of mental health care came into being: those who could pay went to "nerve doctors" in their private offices, while the others had to make do with what they could get at public facilities. The very designation "nerve doctor" removed much of the stigma attached to mental illness through its ambiguity and its implication that "nerves" denoted something connected with the body (as it had done up to the early nineteenth century) rather than with the mind. The new chair created for Charcot in 1882 was, significantly, for "diseases of the nervous system."

As such a disease of the nervous system, neurasthenia was a godsend to both half-mads and nerve doctors. For the latter it provided a lucrative stream of patients, while to the former it offered an attractive explanation of the multitude of their often chronic symptoms. George Beard (see headnote), who sponsored—not to say, invented—neurasthenia, presented it as a *physical* condition—no doubt about that. As the subtitle of his article formulates it, neurasthenia was a deficiency in "nerve force" that arises partly out of a constitutional tendency, that is, a hereditary proclivity, but mainly as a result of overwork and overload through the stresses and strains of modern life. Yet despite the fatigue and weakness that this affliction frequently causes, its victims are likely to lead long, successful lives. The very fact that Beard recommends electrical treatment for neurasthenia confirms his insistence that it is a bodily malady that can be alleviated, if not totally cured, by measures designed presumably to stimulate the nerves and thereby to mitigate the corporeal shortfall. Although Beard does once mention hysteria among the possible manifestations of neurasthenia, his list of symptoms is so absurdly comprehensive that no real importance can be attached to this one facet. On the other hand, it is indicative of Beard's emphasis on the somatic that he wholly sidesteps the entire question of the involvement of psychology in neurasthenia. At the very outset he introduces himself as a neurologist, well trained in electrical treatments, in other words, as one who ministers to the body, not the mind. He is not at all concerned with psychology, which remained for most of the nineteenth century associated primarily with philosophy. The mind/body connection was by no means unknown,[4] but it was increasingly marginalized in the practice of medicine as scientific methods superseded the humoral theories that had envisaged "temperament" as an indissoluble fusion of physical and personality traits. Beard takes into account the neurasthenic's innate disposition: he is likely to be a driven brain-worker (Beard writes of males because there were few such subjects among women of his time); however, for him this is a matter of typology, not of individual psychology. He firmly rationalizes and medicalizes a concatenation of symptoms by interpreting them as expressions of somatic disturbances, whereas nowadays they would most likely be recognized as psychosomatic in nature. It was precisely this dissociation of neurasthenia from any whiff of the psychiatric that assured this new disease entity such widespread, indeed enthusiastic acceptance in the later nineteenth century.

Beard's approach is important as a signpost to the dominant trend of his age, the almost exclusive concentration on bodily mechanisms at the expense of feelings, which were for long very much relegated to the background. The revolutionary discoveries in germ theory that had begun to be disseminated by the time Beard wrote his article inevitably made a deep impression on medical thinking. Although the specific bacteria that caused various infections were not identified until somewhat later,[5] the concept of bacteria as disease-carrying microorganisms was current by the middle of the nineteenth century. This perception slowly ousted the old belief that infectious diseases arose from miasma, the foul air arising from swamps. The very idea of contagion, of the spread of disease through contact, was a novelty so shocking as to be rejected initially when it was put forward in 1847 by Ignaz Semmelweis (1818–65) as the source of the puerperal fever that was felling women in Vienna's main hospital.

The new understanding of the processes of infection had a powerful impact on all areas of medicine. Just as miasma was discredited as the cradle of infection, so demonic possession became by analogy dubious as the origin of mental and emotional imbalance. The successful search for bacteria prompted a parallel endeavor in the forum of mental health, based on the conviction that lesions must exist in the brain (or possibly elsewhere in the body) that caused disorders of the mind. So the German Wilhelm Griesinger (1817–68) instituted the field of neuropsychiatry, which sought to extend the emergent specialty of neurology, which centered on study of the brain, to the domain of psychiatry. As early as 1850 he carried out neuroanatomical research into the structure of the brain in his pathological laboratory. The hunt for lesions became a fixed idea, virtually an obsession, for nineteenth-century psychiatry as it leaned more and more on the fledgling discipline of neurology.[6] Psychiatry was taunted and despised for its lack of scientific progress, its failure to make discoveries even at autopsies. In an autopsy performed on a man who had died in an insane asylum Krafft-Ebing records the state of the brain, but the changes are disappointingly minimal, with no perceptible signs of a lesion. Beard was only one of many who were convinced that lesions would be discovered once microscopes were improved. He implies the presence of a lesion by stating that "all forms of insanity are dependent on some central morbid condition." Charcot, who was also trained as a neurologist (as, indeed, was Freud), expressed the same faith in the presence of lesions and the future capacity of better instruments to pinpoint them.

The preeminent neurologist of his day, Charcot identified and described several syndromes among diseases of the nervous system, one of which bears his name (see headnote). In the wake of such successes, he was naturally inclined to look for similar lesions in all the innumerable cases that came under his charge at the famous La Salpêtrière hospital, of which he became director in 1862. But it was only late in his life, in the 1880s and 1890s, that Charcot began to take an interest in the class of patients known as hysterics. It is one of the great ironies in the history of nineteenth-century psychiatry that this development was due to happenstance when, during one of the periodic renovations and reorganizations at La Salpêtrière, the hysterics were separated from the other patients and placed under Charcot's care. He grew so fascinated with hysteria that it became his major preoccupation until his untimely death in 1893.

Hysteria, together with hypnotism and heredity, is one of the three major motifs of later nineteenth-century psychiatry. Hysteria has rightly been called "the last theater of [demonic] possession"[7] because of its puzzling, multifaceted, changeable symptomatology that made it so difficult to handle, let alone to grasp. A capacious rubric to which mystifying patients could be assigned, hysteria seemed to be the ultimate chameleon, so pervasive and so intent on defying medical understanding that it was dubbed "the wastepaper basket of medicine where one throws otherwise unemployed symptoms."[8] Unlike neurasthenia, it was not a new entity. The amazing history of hysteria has been most ably traced by Ilza Veith[9] as far back as ancient Egyptian and Mesopotamian culture, where it has been found on a number of surviving papyri. The word itself is derived from the Greek for "uterus," *hystera*, since it was thought that hysteria stemmed from a wandering womb. This belief reflects the long-standing convention of attributing hysteria solely to women, a belief that was exposed to question by Pierre Briquet in his *Traité clinique et thérapeutique de l'hystérie* (1859) and subsequently by both Charcot and Freud, although all agreed that it afflicted incomparably more women than men. According to the established superstitious theory, the discontented womb would wander upward in the body, triggering symptoms wherever it chanced to settle. The optimal treatment was marriage and pregnancy, or, failing that, horseback-riding.

Clearly, such a fanciful view would be anathema to a physician as imbued with the scientific ideal as Charcot was. He sought to discern the underlying lesion, but in this sphere he was unable to make any progress. Curiously, this nineteenth-century quest for the elusive lesion seems to have a paradoxical connection to the old notion of the wandering womb because it, too, was predicated on an essentially physical perception: it is a part of the body, not the mind, that has somehow got out of joint. Charcot sought to apply as scientific a method as possible to the clinical study of hysteria at La Salpêtrière. He schematized hysterical attacks into four successive phases and catalogued the recurrent symptoms and positions. But despite his pronounced visual bent and his meticulous observation of the patients' behavior, Charcot was far too astute to stop at these mere externals. He was intuitively aware of other factors that played a part in the etiology of hysteria, even if he recorded them without comment. In each of the three cases included here, an outer event inaugurates the outbreak of hysteria: the industrial accident that almost costs the worker his life when barrels cascade onto him, the wrongful news of her husband's death that induces one woman's amnesia, and the slap meted out to her child that results in the other woman's paralysis of that arm. On the basis of such cases, Charcot created a whole new diagnosis of "hystero-traumatization" in which the damage to the patient is not inflicted directly by the physical accident, but represents the mental and emotional experience of the traumatizing episode. Here

Charcot is on the verge of recognizing the psychological factors ingrained in hysteria; however, because of his allegiance to hard science, he remains quite skeptical. While he urges his students not to fear psychology, he dismisses it as something taught in college, that is, as philosophy, and ultimately he reduces it to nothing but "the rational physiolgy of the cerebral cortex."[10] Although the shadowy presence of psychology is not absolutely denied, its role is subservient and assimilated to physical processes. This statement, made in 1888, summarizes the nineteenth-century predilection for subjugating psychology to physiology.

It was just one year after Charcot's assertion, in 1889, that Arthur Schnitzler published his account of six cases of aphonia. Schnitzler certainly knew Charcot's work; in the *Internationale klinische Rundschau* (International clinical review), which he edited, he regularly reviewed that work with approval (see headnote). Schnitzler, a laryngologist, reports on mysterious instances of women, mostly young and single, who suffer repeated loss of voice over many months, even years, without any discernible physical cause. Being a conscientious internist, Schnitzler examines them with utmost care each time they go to his hospital clinic, yet he finds little or nothing to explain their aphonia. However, generally he avoids resorting to the term *hysteria,* as Charcot would readily have done with inexplicable symptoms; he opts instead for *functional,* which is used in implied contrast to *organic.* Since he was not a neurologist or psychiatrist, Schnitzler may have preferred the term current in his own field. This switch to *functional* is a small but telling turning point insofar as *hysterical* carries judgmental, derogatory overtones, of which *functional* is free; it is purely a descriptive medical denotation of the patient's condition.

Functional denotes the absence of a pathological lesion and may suggest the presence of a neurosis, although Schnitzler does not go that far. As a laryngologist, he was used to looking first for signs of physical disease, but in these women he notes only minor changes in the vocal chords of minimal significance. These he records objectively, yet his failure to turn up physical reasons for the aphonia does not lead him to speculate on other possible origins of the disability. Without despising or distrusting psychology, as Charcot does, Schnitzler ignores it except in his crucial realization of the psychological dimension in the effectiveness of hypnosis and suggestion as stemming from the patient's trusting relationship to the hypnotizer. Two of his cases show unmistakable psychological factors involved in their aphonia: one improves greatly when she leaves home to live with an aunt, while the other is cured by marriage. Schnitzler bypasses this whole area, approaching afflictions that seem to be psychosomatic in origin as if they were somatic. Similarly, Krafft-Ebing invariably emphasizes the somatic factors in the etiology of deviant sexual behavior. While he occasionally mentions concomitant "psychological disturbances" in some of his subjects, who seem to show signs of a possible involvement of the psyche, he definitely gives strong preference to physical causes (see headnote).

Of the late nineteenth-century physicians Pierre Janet attains the best balance between the physical and the psychological. His background was certainly instrumental in this, for he was a professor of philosophy before taking a medical degree (see headnote). His patients exhibit myriad ills, all of which would promptly have been subsumed at the time into the category of hysteria. Justine, the subject of the case history in this collection, has not only a long-standing series of fixed ideas but also violent convulsive attacks of bodily and mental disarray. Janet notes the various physical manifestations of her disequilibrium, but, unlike Charcot and Schnitzler, he is concerned not only to inquire into the history of her physical illnesses but also to probe the psychological undergrowth, going back into her childhood traumas in order to unearth the hidden mainsprings of her present disorders. Janet, who was a contemporary of Freud and who actually mentions Breuer and Freud in this case history, thus comes nearest to Freud by investigating the role of the past in the genesis of the current symptoms. However, unlike Freud, he resists formulating any general principles; at both the opening and the end of his case history he emphasizes his wariness of making generalizations or of drawing large conclusions from a few cases. As an experimental psychologist, Janet favors extensive engagement with individual patients, examining each one in great detail. By this approach, Janet, the most psychologically perspicacious physician of this period, effected a farreaching change in nineteenth-century psychiatry. It is certainly no coincidence that his case histories, as are Freud's, are often known by the patient's name—Justine, Léonie, Marcelle, Lucie, Irène, Marie— because each one stands out as a very distinctive personality. Such close attention to a single individual consummates a crucial metamorphosis in psychiatry. From the blanket control of lunatics and their demons, psychiatry moved to the study of groups, who were presumed to have similar lesions, of which specific cases represented examples, and ultimately with Janet and Freud to the analysis of singular persons with peculiar neuroses.

Even though hysteria remained no more than a convenient label to pin onto refractive patients, especially women, a syndrome that continued to be poorly defined and still more poorly understood, it was treated in the same way by Charcot, Schnitzler, and Janet. They all resorted to hypnosis, the second of the three overarching features of later nineteenth-century psychiatry. Like hysteria itself, hypnotism has a very long history, full of strange episodes.[11] Its most famous, or notorious, exponent in the modern age was Franz Anton Mesmer (1734–1813), an Austrian doctor, who was thought by some to be a magician and by others a charlatan. Mesmer, who was a prominent public persona first in Vienna and then in Paris, held mystical ideas. His doctoral dissertation was on the influence of the planets on the human body, and he believed in the existence of what he called a universal fluid in which all things are immersed as in a cosmic ocean, and that governed gravitation, magnetism, electricity, light, and heat.[12] Mesmer asserted that illnesses could be cured by animal magnetism, that is, by the transmission of power from one person to another via the universal fluid. He achieved some remarkable successes, notably with a young relative of his wife's, Franziska Oesterlin, who suffered from a whole spectrum of ills that were almost certainly psychosomatic: convulsions, spasms, vomiting, inability to urinate, toothache and earache, despondency, hallucinations, cataleptic trances, fainting spells, temporary blindness, feelings of suffocation, and bouts of paralysis. But Mesmer never managed to have his magnetic cures acknowledged by the medical faculty, and he was also discredited by rumors of sexual licentiousness in the course of his treatments.

Hypnotism was put onto a firmer footing by the work of a series of nineteenth-century doctors. The first was the English surgeon James Braid (1795–1860), whose book *Neurypnology* appeared in 1843. Braid's contribution was twofold: he substituted the term *hypnotism* for *mesmerism* or *animal magnetism*, thus ridding the procedure of its disreputable associations, and, even more crucially, he demonstrated that hypnotism results from suggestion. Part I of his book (1–160) is devoted to the means of inducing hypnosis both in theory and in practice; Braid cites some twenty-five examples, fairly evenly spread in gender and age. Part II (162–200) then illustrates the therapeutic applications in a very large number of cases; they are recorded with utmost brevity, but the cures are attested by reliable witnesses. Braid's work became known in France when he read a paper to the French Academy of Sciences in 1860, the same year in which a Dr. Durand le Gros also published a book on "Braidism."

Braid's lecture was heard by Dr. Ambroise-Auguste Liébeault (1823–1904), a country practitioner without specialized expertise who was nonetheless decisive in the infiltration of hypnotism into medicine. Liébeault conceived hypnotism as stemming from the power of suggestion, "l'influence de l'esprit sur le corps" (the influence of the mind on the body), as he puts it on the first page of his book *Le Sommeil provoqué et les états analogues* (Induced Sleep and Its Analogous States), a book whose origins go back to 1866, although it did not appear until 1889. Liébeault's usage of *sommeil* (sleep) for the state he induced in his patients fostered the term *somnambulism* as an alternative to *hypnotism*. Although he writes in the preface of "les applications de cette science à l'art de guérir" (2; the applications of this science to the art of healing), he does not deal with the therapeutic aspects, concentrating instead on generalized reflections on trancelike states.

Liébeault's dry book, which sold five copies in five years, would have made little impact had it not been for Hippolyte Bernheim (1837–1919), an internist at the University of Strasbourg. When the university was transferred to Nancy after the French defeat in the Franco-Prussian War, Bernheim was in the vicinity of Liébeault, heard of his hypnotic skills through a patient whom he had cured of sciatica, and subsequently visited him in 1882. As the holder of a chair in medicine, Bernhaim commanded the professional respect that the modest Liébeault lacked. So it was Bernheim who became the most influential advocate for the use of suggestion in the treatment of physical disorders too. Bernheim has been extensively translated into English: his *Suggestion dans l'état hypnotique et dans l'état de veille* (1884) appeared in 1888 as *Suggestive Therapeutics;* his central work, *Hypnotisme, suggestion, psychothérapie* (1891), hailed as "a classic in the history of hypnotism and of psychotherapy,"[13] and translated as *Hypnosis and Suggestion in Psychotherapy: A Treatise on the Nature and Uses of Hypnotism* (1973), was followed in 1980 by a collection of his translated papers under the title *New Studies in Hypnotism*. All Bernheim's works are distinguished by their clarity and their far-ranging horizon; together with Liébeault, he amassed a large number of cases in which hypnotism was successful after conventional treatments had failed. As a specialist in internal medicine, Bernheim believed that the beneficial impact of hypnotism was due to demonstrable physiologic processes that were prompted by suggestion. He had a deep interest in analyzing the physiological effects of hypnosis on the body, particularly on the cardiovascular system and on respiration. Arguably, this conception of hypnotism as an essentially physical phenomenon can be seen as a reprise from the lineage of Mesmer, albeit on a radically updated, scientifically sound basis.

Hypnotism became a central issue in French medicine with the rivalry between the Nancy school of Bernheim and the Parisian school of Charcot. The latter regarded hypnosis as the most suitable treatment for nervous diseases, above all hysteria, while the former backed its wider potential in physical disorders too. The debate raged with considerable rancor. The most recent historian of hypnosis has concluded that "in due course, for the ultimate good of hypnosis, the views of Charcot and his pupils at the Salpêtrière were gradually defeated by the Nancy school. After Charcot's death in 1893, one by one his former students and colleagues recanted their views."[14] A sequel to the victory of the Nancy school can perhaps be seen in the twentieth-century method of biofeedback, which aims to control physiological states, such as blood pressure, by autohypnosis. Still, it was the paper that Charcot delivered to the Académie des Sciences on his election in 1892 that gave hypnotism dignity and acceptance in the medical profession because of his enormous personal prestige. Later in that decade Freud turned to hypnosis in the treatment of his patients in the *Studies on Hysteria* (1896). Because he experienced difficulty in inducing hypnosis in some strong-willed patients, notably Elisabeth R., he devised an alternative: laying hands on her head, he urged her to close her eyes and to say whatever entered her mind. Thus hypnosis was morphed into the free association of psychoanalysis.

One area in which Freud departs from his predecessors is in his privileging of family dynamics over heredity. Heredity was of such prominence in the later nineteenth century as to form the third characteristic tenet in the psychiatry of the period. Yet precise knowledge of heredity was still scant, based on empirical observation rather than science. The laws of heredity were actually discovered by the Austrian monk Gregor Mendel (1822–84) through his experiments with the hybridization of peas. He read papers on the topic in 1865 and 1866 to the Natural Science Society of Brunn in Moravia and published his findings in 1866 in the society's journal. It is another of the ironies of history that this journal was so obscure that Mendel's momentous discovery, the foundation of modern genetics, was completely overlooked at the time and did not enter into the mainstream of scientific thinking until the first decade of the twentieth century. In the absence of familiarity with Mendel's theories, it is tempting to assume that Darwin's *Origin of Species by Means of Natural Selection* (1859) must have given impetus to the growing belief in human heredity too. However, the eminent cultural historian Charles Rosenberg considers Darwin's role to have been "problematical," arguing that "interest in hereditarian modes of social explanation was firmly established in the 1840s. Forces independent of the formal debate on species and evolution—and antedating it—must therefore have played an autonomous role. Moreover, Darwin's own formulations—though they clearly had the effect of increasing the prevalence, legitimacy, and emotional relevance of hereditarian explanatory models—had little, if any, effect on reshaping generally accepted attitudes toward human heredity."[15] In any case, heredity, as a tool of natural selection, was in Darwin's scheme a vehicle for an upward evolution, whereas in later nineteenth-century psychiatry it was connected to an atavistic mental degeneracy.

Mental degeneracy was "throughout the last half of the nineteenth century the most important term in the French psychiatric vocabulary."[16] This predilection was not confined to France, although it was most strongly elaborated there. Morbid heredity as the prism for mental degeneracy was lent credence by Théodule Ribot's treatise on heredity that appeared in 1873 and built on a great deal of earlier speculation. A further notion was advanced by Charles Féré in his 1884 presentation to the Société médico-psychologique of the concept of the "neuropathic family" that perpetuated and cumulatively aggravated the hereditary disposition to disease and mental disequilibrium of all kinds. Krafft-Ebing's entire opus on deviant sexual behavior was seen as evidence of the consequences of mental degeneracy since many of his cases are from families with a bad history.

A prime example of such a family is provided by Janet, who devotes the fifth section of his case study to Justine's family history under the title "Evolution of an Illness: Personal and Hereditary Antecedents." Even though the information proves difficult to elicit and often uncertain, he sets up a family tree that reaches back to her grandparents and reveals a proliferating morbidity through her siblings, their children, and their grandchildren, a total of forty-six people descended from the initial couple. Infant deaths are common, rising up to 74 percent in the fourth generation (at a time when the average infant mortality rate was 20 percent). More striking still is the incidence of what Janet calls "disintegrating minds," characterized by obsessiveness, impulsiveness, violence, epilepsy, idiocy, and most frequently, alcoholism. Hysteria was thought to be the inevitable out-

come of such a blighted heredity. Exactly the same ideas inspire
Émile Zola's twenty-novel cycle *Les Rougon-Macquart: Histoire naturelle
et sociale d'une famille sous le Second Empire* (1871–93; *The Rougon-Macquart: The Natural and Social History of a Family under the Second Empire*).
Zola, too, draws up a tree of the four generations of his fictional family, placing its middle-class, fairly healthy members on the legitimate
side and the marginalized, mainly working-class degenerates on the
illegitimate side. The positioning of the adjective *natural* before *social*
in the designation of the family's history is indicative of the salient
role accorded to heredity.

While none of the other writers in this collection give as much
attention and space to the question of heredity as Janet does, all of
them take it into account as a factor of some weight. They are obviously convinced of its fundamental importance in the etiology of
mental as well as of physical disorders. Beard, for instance, asserts that
"hereditary descent terribly predisposes to neurasthenia"; sick headache, epilepsy, insanity, or dyspepsia in a grandfather may show as
neurasthenia in the grandchildren. He believes that the shortfall in
nervous force that he sees as the root of neurasthenia results at least
partly from a constitutional tendency. *Constitutional* is a polite euphe-
mism for *hereditary*, less liable to ruffle his middle- to upper-class clientele than *hereditary*, which generally implied a taint of some sort and
thus had decidedly negative connotations. Schnitzler, with his lower-
class patients, does not need to be as tactful. He begins his account
of each one with a pointed notation of the family's health history as
a possibly explanatory frame for the patient's complaint. Although
he is dealing with a very specific problem, aphonia, he implicitly
assumes a link between the patient's present deficit and the family's
hereditary tendency to illness.

That link is made explicit in all three of Charcot's cases in this volume, for he is quite outspoken in endorsing the pronounced significance of heredity in the etiology of hysteria. In discussing the woman
who sustains paralysis of the arm after slapping her child, he mentions early on that she has "a whole past and a heritage that reveal
many things" (25). Her heredity, he asserts, "is of some importance"
(27), and although such "pathological antecedents" cannot be held
against her, "heredity is interesting because it always brings us back
to the same principle: it proves that hysteria doesn't appear out of
nowhere like a mushroom" (26). Here hysteria is categorically perceived as a hereditarily grounded malady. In the patient with amnesia, too, Charcot discerns a "stain of debauchery and drunkenness"

(59) from her violent, alcoholic father; she has, he concludes, "a terrain already predisposed by heredity" (60). Such "nervous heredity" (34) is underscored even more strongly in the male hysteric. Alongside other factors, Charcot asserts, "heredity is definitely one element in the majority of cases" (37). This man's "hereditary antecedents" (45–46) are indeed ominous in his mother's descent from nervous attacks into drinking and finally insanity. Thus the "predisposition" to hysteria will always remain because "the influence of heredity is there, always present" (50). This assumption of the cardinal role of heredity undermines hopes of lasting improvement; hysteria is likely to recur because it is genetically ingrained. The doctrine of heredity therefore is the platform for the undercurrent of pessimism in later nineteenth-century psychiatry and consequently for the physicians' sense of impotence in the face of their patients' illnesses.

That pessimism is strongest in Krafft-Ebing, who is in many respects the odd man out in this collection. As a forensic psychiatrist, he approaches his subjects from a different perspective insofar as they are under judicial investigation and not hospitalized or voluntary patients in a clinic (see headnote). Krafft-Ebing mentions hysteria as rarely as Beard does; just as it is one symptom of neurasthenia, similarly it is an occasional but not a primary manifestation among the sexual deviants Krafft-Ebing examines. Nor does he refer to hypnotism since he is not at all concerned with therapies; he does not envisage sexual deviancy as remediable by any particular treatment; some of his subjects enter a state of remission, desisting from destructive behavior, while others have to be committed to an asylum. As Schnitzler does, Krafft-Ebing invariably begins his report by a survey of the subject's age, class, occupation, and personal history, including heredity. For instance, case 2 is introduced as "Mr. X., eighty, of high social standing, from a family with a hereditary taint." Case 7, F., twenty-three, single, a cobbler, has a father with a vicious temper and a mother who was a "neuropath" and had an insane brother. Case 20, Z., a law student, twenty years old, "comes from a tainted family" with a sister who is "mentally ill" and a brother who suffers from male hysteria. Case 48, Mr. von X., of high social standing, a Russian, twenty-eight years old, "comes from a family with a history of frequent neuroses and psychoses." In at least half of his subjects Krafft-Ebing finds clear evidence of such hereditary degeneracy. Occasionally a patient is described as "not hereditarily tainted" (case 51), or, exceptionally, as "from a good family." However, even the very absence of hereditary factors is for Krafft-Ebing eminently worth recording because he regards its presence as the norm. And sometimes he doubts the subject's claim as in case 4, P., thirty-six, a day laborer who "maintains that he comes from a healthy family"; the insertion of *maintains*, though customary in medical writing, implies a degree of skepticism. For Krafft-Ebing heredity is unquestionably a prominent key to his subjects' aberrant behavior.

Reading these case histories leads to a deeper appreciation of Freud's originality by enabling us to see more clearly both the continuities and the innovations in his work when it is juxtaposed to that of his immediate predecessors. The continuities are most apparent in his early joint publication of 1896 with Breuer, the *Studies on Hysteria*. The very diagnostic term *hysteria* shows Freud as following on Charcot, with whom he had studied for five months in 1885–86. His use of hypnosis also clearly derives from Charcot as well as from Bernheim, whom he had also visited. Thus in his initial practices Freud stands within the lineage of later nineteenth-century psychiatry. In addition to suggestion, he resorts to physical treatment, most strikingly in the first case in *Studies on Hysteria*, Emmy von N., himself massaging her daily. Moreover, in *Studies on Hysteria* Freud reports on a series of six cases, using the plurality as a basis for his reflective generalizations, again in a manner reminiscent of his antecedents' customs. All the physicians included here, except Janet, preface their clinical findings with theoretical observations. But although Freud presents a sequence of six cases, all of whom exhibit various forms of "hysteria," he particularizes them far beyond the mere facts of an initial, age, and civil status. Each has a first name; above all, each is sited in a frame that consists less of family illnesses than of family tensions and difficulties in interpersonal relationships. For this reason Freud's case histories read, as he himself ruefully admits, more like stories devoid of the serious imprint of science. As the novelist does, he gives a rich picture of his patients' lives in all their complexity so as to fathom the factors causative of their neuroses.

It is this focus on family dynamics that most sharply distinguishes Freud from his predecessors. He realizes that bodily symptoms without organic cause—what was then called hysteria and would nowadays be deemed conversion disorders—are in fact indirect physical expressions of psychological malaise.[17] This revolutionary realization brings in its wake a reversal of the former approach to the patient. Instead of concentrating first and foremost on the patient's physical condition, Freud looks straight toward the state of mind. In fact, very soon he dispenses entirely with the normative physical examination, which had been the basis of psychiatric methodology so long as mental disorders were thought to spring from some somatic lesion. Once Freud recognizes neurosis as his patients' underlying problem, the physical complaints are seen as the oblique carriers of a message that cannot be put into words either out of shame or, more likely, because the sufferer herself/himself is unaware of or subconsciously resistant to acknowledging the hurt. It is precipitated and articulated through the medium of the body, although its core is essentially psychological. This insight results in Freud's intentness on the patient's feelings, which, again with the exception of Janet, had been largely or even totally ignored in previous case histories.

Freud's understanding of the centrality of family dynamics as the wellspring of neuroses has further consequences. Heredity recedes into the background in favor of more recent personal experiences. In other words, nature yields to nurture, that is, to the traumas sustained by the patient through both conditioning in infancy and subsequent damaging situations. Not by coincidence are a considerable proportion of Freud's patients women since they were in his time socialized to conformity and silence. In order to combat this repression, Freud encourages the spontaneous voicing of thoughts and feelings in the free association of psychoanalysis. He does not put clipped, closed questions to his patients, as Schnitzler and Charcot did; much rather, he fosters the release of pent-up emotions by making the patient take the lead in speaking freely of whatever comes to mind. Psychoanalysis is therefore not merely a therapeutic method; it devolves from a philosophical perception that turns its back completely on the notion of somatic lesions, affirming instead the vitality of the psyche's subconscious processes and their power to determine human conduct in ways sometimes strange or contrary to rational expectations. So the unconscious is instituted as the ultimate motivational source. In this formal systematization of its role Freud goes so far beyond his predecessors' vague intuitions as to effect a veritable transformation of psychiatry.

NOTES

1. Elizabeth Lunbeck, *The Psychiatric Persuasion: Knowledge, Gender, and Power in Modern America* (Princeton, N.J.: Princeton University Press, 1994), 81.

2. Dorrit Cohn, "Freud's Case Histories and the Question of Fictionality," in *Telling Facts: History and Facts in Psychoanalysis,* ed. Joseph Smith and Humphrey Morris, 43 n. 12 (Baltimore and London: The Johns Hopkins University Press, 1992).

3. Jan Goldstein, *Console and Classify: The French Psychiatric Profession in the Nineteenth Century* (Chicago: University of Chicago Press, 2001), 334.

4. See Charles E. Rosenberg, "Body and Mind in Nineteenth-Century Medicine," in *Explaining Epidemics and Other Studies in the History of Medicine* (New York: Cambridge University Press, 1992), 74–89.

5. For dates of various diseases see Erwin H. Ackerknecht, *A Short History of Medicine* (Baltimore and London: The Johns Hopkins University Press, 1982), 180.

6. The board certification held by American psychiatrists attests to their competence in "Psychiatry and Neurology." The examinations are quite different, but no formal separation has ever taken place. The American Psychiatric Association was established in 1844, its counterpart, the American Neurological Association, in 1875.

7. Jacqueline Carroy-Thirard, "Possession, extase, hystérie au 19è siècle," *Psychanalyse à l'université* 5 (June 1980): 301.

8. Attributed to the French psychiatrist Charles Lasègue, cited by Jan Goldstein, *Console and Classify: The French Psychiatric Profession in the Nineteenth Century* (Chicago: University of Chicago Press, 2001).

9. Ilza Veith, *Hysteria: The History of a Disease* (Chicago and London: University of Chicago Press, 1970).

10. "En matière de maladies nerveuses, la psychologie est là, et ce que j'appelle la psychologie, c'est la physiologie rationnelle de l'écorce cérébrale." Trillat, *Histoire de l'hystérie*, 95.

11. See Robin Waterfield, *Hidden Depths: The Story of Hypnosis* (New York: Brunner-Routledge, 2003).

12. See Maria Tatar, *Spellbound: Studies in Mesmerism and Literature* (Princeton, N.J.: Princeton University Press, 1978), 3–43, and Vincent Buranelli, *The Wizard from Vienna.* (New York: Coward, McCann & Geoghan, 1975).

13. Bernheim, Hippolyte, *Hypnosis and Suggestion in Psychotherapy: A Treatise on the Nature and Uses of Hypnotism,* trans. Christian A. Herter (New York: Jason Aronson, 1973), ix.

14. Robin Waterfield, *Hidden Depths: The Story of Hypnosis* (New York: Brunner-Routledge, 2003), 223.

15. Charles E. Rosenberg, "The Bitter Fruit: Heredity, Disease, and Social Thought," in *No Other Gods: On Science and American Social Thought* (Baltimore: The Johns Hopkins University Press, 1976), 34.

16. Ian Dowbiggin, "Degeneration and hereditarianism," in *Madhouses, Mad-Doctors and Madmen: The Social History of Psychiatry in the Victorian Era* (Philadelphia: University of Pennsylvania Press, 1981), 188.

17. See Furst, "Speaking Through the Body," *Idioms of Distress* (Albany: State Univ. Press of New York, 2003) 1–18.

1

George Miller Beard

GEORGE BEARD'S BRIEF ARTICLE, "NEURASTHENIA, OR NERVOUS EXHAUS-
tion," originally delivered orally as a paper, was published in the pres-
tigious *Boston Medical and Surgical Journal* of April 29, 1869 (3, no. 13:
217–21) and is a landmark in the history of psychiatry. If Beard did
not himself invent neurasthenia, he certainly coined the term and
here launched the syndrome on its long road of popularity.

As a concept, neurasthenia builds on and develops the older "nervous exhaustion," a phrase that had become too "indefinite"—and
lacking in glamour—for Beard's time, which set such great store by
science. Not the least of its attractions was that neurasthenia, derived,
as Beard carefully points out near the outset, from the Greek and
therefore sounds so much more scientific than *nervous exhaustion*.
This use of Greek serves also to testify to Beard's learnedness. Moreover, by citing his malady in relation to the "nervous exhaustion"
known to his predecessors, whose names he cites, he gives it a
respectable lineage and at the same time claims its novelty under its
new name. Its scientific nature is emphasized again later on in connection with the young doctor, a patient of Beard's, who "carefully
watches and studies his symptoms" and is lauded as "a scientific man."

Beard was by no means a charlatan, as has sometimes been hinted;
he appears truly to have believed in what he preached despite a certain element of expediency. Born in Montville, Connecticut, in 1839,
he had a good education at Phillips Andover Academy and at Yale,
where he graduated in 1862. After serving for eighteen months as an
assistant surgeon on a gunboat in 1863–64, he obtained his medical
degree at the New York College of Physicians and Surgeons in 1866.
In the later 1860s and early 1870s he practiced on Madison Avenue
in New York in partnership with Alphonse David Rockwell, who
edited his unfinished work after his early death at age forty-four.
Beard and Rockwell purchased the electrical machinery of an itiner-
ant electrotherapist, who was retiring, and took on his clientele,

applying electrotherapy rather indiscriminately. This is the experience he invokes in this article along with his previous training in the Department of Neurology and Electrotherapeutics at New York University to establish his professional credentials. In 1871 Beard and Rockwell published *A Practical Treatise on the Medical and Surgical Uses of Electricity,* which was a great success, especially in Germany.

When Beard presented this paper on neurasthenia in 1869, he was still at the beginning of his short but very productive career. The son of a clergyman, he had an evangelical fervor together with extraordinary energy, enterprise, and versatility. He wrote on a wide range of topics for both a popular and a medical audience: *Electricity as a Tonic* (1866), *Our Home Physician* (1869), *Eating and Drinking* (1871), *Stimulants and Narcotics* (1871), *Hay-fever or Summer catarrh* (1876), *The Scientific Basis of Delusions* (1877). However, it was for his special interest in diseases of the nervous system that he was and is best known.

Beard later developed the seminal ideas in this article in his two major works: *A Practical Treatise on Nervous Exhaustion: Neurasthenia, Its Symptoms, Nature, Sequences, Treatment* (1881; rpt. New York: Arno Press, 1971) and *American Nervousness, with Its Causes and Consequences* (1883; rpt. New York: Arno Press, 1972).[1] If the 1869 article is, in Beard's words, "*suggestive*" rather than "exhaustive," this latter word certainly fits the two comprehensive volumes, which are complementary, in fact to some extent overlapping. *American Nervousness,* announced by Beard as "A Supplement to *Nervous Exhaustion,*" is designated by him as being "of a more distinctly philosophical and popular character" (preface, iii–iv) than the earlier treatise "which was specially addressed to the professional and scientific reader" (iv). *Nervous Exhaustion* is more medical in tone, *American Nervousness* more speculative. Both enjoyed immediate and lasting success: *Nervous Exhaustion* required a second printing within three months and went through five subsequent editions. Although introduced by Beard as a specifically American affliction, neurasthenia had potent appeal in Europe too: in 1891 Fernand Levillain, a follower of Charcot, published *Neurasthénie: Maladie de Beard,* and Franz Carl Miller's *Handbuch der Neurasthenie* (Handbook of neurasthenia) appeared in Germany in 1893.

In the two treatises as in the 1869 article neurasthenia is a tremendously checkered patchwork, manifest in a quite bewildering assortment of symptoms. The opening chapter of *American Nervousness* lists the following:

Insomnia, flushing, drowsiness, bad dreams, cerebral irritation, dilated pupils, pain, pressure and heaviness in the head, changes in the expression of the eye, neurasthenic asthenopia, noises in the ear, atonic voice, mental irritability, tenderness of the teeth and gums, nervous dyspepsia, desire for stimulants and narcotics, abnormal dryness of the skin, joints and mucous membranes, sweating hands and feet with redness, fear of lightning, or fear of responsibility, of open places or of closed places, fear of society, fear of being alone, fear of fears, fear of contamination, fear of everything, deficient mental control, lack of decision in trifling matters, hopelessness, deficient thirst and capacity for assimilating fluids, abnormalities of the secretions, salivation, tenderness of the spine, and of the whole body, sensitiveness to cold or hot water, coceyodenia, pains in the back, heaviness of the loins and limbs, shooting pains simulating those of ataxia, cold hands and feet, localized peripheral numbness and hyperaesthesia, tremulous and irritable pulse and palpitations of the heart, special idiosyncrasies in regard to food, medicines, and external irritants, local spasms of muscles, difficulties of swallowing, convulsive movements, especially on going to sleep, cramps, a feeling of profound exhaustion unaccompanied by positive pain, coming and going, ticklishness, vague pains and flying neuralgias, general or local itching, general and local chills and flashes of heat, attacks of temporary paralysis in the perineum, involuntary emissions, partial or complete impotence, irritability of the prostatic urethra, certain functional diseases of women, gaping and yawning, rapid decay and irregularities of the teeth, oxalates, urates, phosphates and spermotozoa in the urine, vertigo or dizziness, explosions in the brain at the back of the neck, dribbling and incontinence of urine, frequent urination, choreic movements of different parts of the body, dryness of the hair, falling away of the hair and beard, slow reaction of the skin, etc. (*American Nervousness*, 7–8)

In *Nervous Exhaustion* the "symptoms" cover pages 36–117! By interspersing this curious list with unfamiliar medical terms (e.g., *asthenopia, coceyodenia*) Beard endows it with a patina of scientific prestige while still leaving most of it comprehensible to a lay audience of prospective patients.

This very profusion of symptoms had certain definite advantages for physicians and patients alike. At a time of intense competition in the profession following the great increase in the number of medical schools from 52 in 1850 to 160 in 1900, and the consequent overproduction of doctors in the United States, neurasthenia was a welcome money spinner since patients tended to be, as Beard himself put it, "'rounders,' going from one physician to another" (*Nervous*

Exhaustion, 113). For patients suffering from vague malaise, neurasthenia afforded a ready and consoling answer to their problems.

From the short article reprinted here as well as from the later lengthy lists of symptoms, one crucial characteristic of neurasthenia becomes clear immediately: it represents a confluence of physical and psychological manifestations. While we nowadays would quickly recognize some of the symptoms such as the multiple fears, bad dreams, hopelessness, insomnia, mental irritability, and perhaps headaches as more likely stemming from a psychological causation, Beard in his peculiar jumble of ills studiously avoids any suggestion that the mind might in any way be involved. On the contrary, he underscores the purely physical origins of neurasthenia by the parallel between anemia, a weakness of the blood, and neurasthenia, a weakness of nervous force. His familiarity with electricity leads him to the felicitous metaphoric analogy with the battery, which works perfectly when charged, yet whose reserves may be so drained as to become "feeble" and "useless" (*American Nervousness,* 10–11). The comparison to a somatic disorder such as anemia was highly important at a period when any form of mental or emotional disorder was regarded as deeply shameful. By aligning neurasthenia with anemia, Beard removes the sting of disgrace; the malady is due simply to exhaustion of the nerve force, an overexpenditure of energy.

Indeed, Beard goes even further by endowing neurasthenia with a positive spin. Although its total effect is exhaustion, its ultimate root is often overwork, overexertion in the dutiful pursuit of business or professional obligations, that is, a worthy, if excessive output of energy. So, according to Beard, neurasthenia most frequently strikes "in civilized, intellectual communities," and its victims are "our leading brain-workers," not the "hardy barbarian." His conjecture was only partially correct. In *Before Freud: Neurasthenia and the American Medical Community,* Francis Gosling gives the following statistics, based on 217 cases: 36.4 percent were professionals, 25.8 percent skilled or semi-skilled, 20 percent housewives, 9.7 percent laborers, and 7.8 percent "other" (32). However, through his association of neurasthenia with high-class work, Beard turns it virtually into a badge of honor as well as "a part of the compensation for our progress and refinement." In *American Nervousness* Beard is even more specific, infusing social theory into his medical creed by attributing the incidence of neurasthenia to "steam power, the periodical press, the telegraph, the sciences, and the mental activity of women" (96).

Such vast generalizations are typical of Beard, who likes to proceed inductively from the universal to the particular. So most of this article consists of large assertions about neurasthenia, said to be derived from Beard's own experience, although it must have been fairly limited at the time since he had been in medical practice for barely three years. His survey covers a grand total of thirty cases, of which only one is presented in any detail, that of the overworked, confined young doctor who manages, through Beard's electrical treatment, to gain some weight after all other remedies have failed to help him in any way. Other cases are merely mentioned in passing: that of the "stout, plethoric gentleman," who responded to alternating galvanic and Faradaic electrical currents, and that of the lawyer/judge, who had suffered from neurasthenia for decades, yet who had led a busy, productive life and attained the age of seventy. Curiously, Beard does not adduce a single female case, although he does include hysteria, which was considered the prime nervous affliction of women, as one possible component of neurasthenia. But it is just one among so very many potential components that it carries no special significance. Beard's article leaves the impression that neurasthenia is a male malady, a noble price to pay for ardent, albeit perhaps overardent devotion to the serious business of living.

That neurasthenia was not exclusively a male malady is shown by Margaret Cleaves's *Autobiography of a Neurasthene,* which appeared in 1910 but deals with happenings that took place in the 1880s. Cleaves, born in 1848, was admittedly a rather unusual woman for the late nineteenth century in that she followed in her beloved father's footsteps by becoming a physician. She ran a busy practice in New York City until, as did that of Beard's young doctor, her health broke down under the sheer pressure of overwork. "Imbued at an early age with a feeling of responsibility towards life" (39), Cleaves came increasingly under the sway of "a stern sense of duty" (59) that led her to live "at top speed and white heat" (65) so that she became a prime candidate for the illness that struck her. Without any ascertainable somatic disease, she exhibited more or less chronic symptoms, most of which fit the profile of neurasthenia: persistent fatigue, insomnia, stress and anxiety, pain, difficulty in eating, a disturbance in her hearing that was deemed auditory fatigue. She herself believes that she has "an unstable nerve organization" (16) so that she suffers from a "lack of neuronic energy" (90), "brain congestion" (44), or "cerebral fatigue" (153), which is translated into physical terms as "disturbed

cerebral circulation" (173). Cleaves unquestioningly adopts Beard's
terminology and diagnosis: that she exhibits what he dubbed "cere-
brasasthenia," brain exhaustion. When her physician tells her that
she has "sprained her brain," she accepts this bizarre diagnosis with
relief, glad above all not to have been told that she has hysteria.

Cleaves is prescribed predominantly rest in the quiet of the country, which she obviously needs. Rest is one of several remedies that
Beard recommends, including such natural hygienic measures as air,
sunlight, water, food, diversion, and muscular exercise. This nurtur-
ing regimen was an advance on the earlier depletive measures such
as bleeding, leeches, and starvation, which often did more harm than
good. This applies also to internal medications: strychnine, quinine,
iron, mercury, phosphorus, and arsenic, which might be noxious, or
to which patients might become addicted. Phosphorus would, in
Beard's opinion, probably have been the most appropriate medication since he ventures as a possible cause of neurasthenia that the
body has become "dephosphorized" (218). He does not explain this
term, although he admits "the absence of definite knowledge" (218)
about the pathology of neurasthenia. In this sphere, as in many other
instances throughout this article, he purports to proceed "by reason
from logical probability" (218). However, his reasoning is often far
from transparent, or even either logical or probable.

The one thing of which Beard is absolutely sure is the optimal treatment for neurasthenia: general electrization. Since this was his specialty and he and Rockwell owned the equipment, the recommendation appears at least to some degree suspiciously self-serving.
Electrical therapy of various types was ubiquitous in the later nineteenth century, as John L. Greenway documents in his illuminating
article " 'Nervous Disease' and Electrical Medicine."[2] Magazines were
full of advertisements for such gadgets as the "Electropathic (battery)
Belt," the "Electric Corset," the "Electric Brush," and the "Electro-
poise" marketed in 1895 to treat "Rheumatism, Indigestion, Nervous
Troubles, General Weakness, Inflammations, Dyspepsia, Sleepless-
ness, Coughs and Colds, Paralysis, Spinal Troubles."[3] This contrap-
tion obviously cashed in on the impression made by electricity,
although it involved no current, producing its local shock effect by
means of a sealed chrome cylinder that was to be filled with ice water.
The cylinder was connected by insulated wire to a small plate to be
placed on the ankle or wrist. Particularly in regard to electricity it was
hard to clarify the border between legitimate science and pseudo-
science. For instance, Du Bois-Reymond, to whom Beard refers, had

shown all muscles and nerves to be the seats of neural currents. On the other hand, Dr. Wilhelm Erb, on whom Beard also rests his argument, had simply managed to imply that electrotherapeutics was the newest of the new by stating that its relationship to physiology was similar to that of physiology to biology. Although his *Handbuch der Elektrotherapie* (*Handbook of electrotherapy*)[4] became a standard text, its scientific basis was dubious, to say the least.

In his fervent advocacy of electrotherapeutics Beard was thus simultaneously and cleverly cashing in on and further promoting a fad of his time. However, even this most efficacious therapy was not invariably successful; sometimes it had to be continued longer than expected; sometimes the two types of current, the galvanic and the Faradaic, had to be applied in alternation; and sometimes relapses occurred. Nonetheless, Beard claims that the great majority of his thirty cases, indeed all except five, show improvement to varying degrees.

Altogether, neurasthenia, as conceived by Beard in his longer works as well as in this article, is marked by an extraordinary instability. Its innumerable symptoms are a crude collage; its diagnosis is therefore "sometimes entirely clear, and again . . . quite difficult (218); it can be acute or chronic; it may be associated with all manner of other diseases in every area of the body and the mind. Its prognosis, Beard continues, "is as various as are the symptoms of the disease" (218). Within this extreme multiformity, however, neurasthenia has one basic unifying feature: it is almost never a fatal malady. Although it has a detrimental impact on the lives of its victims, who feel they "live at a poor, dying rate" (219), it is hardly ever actually a killer. And, striking another optimistic note, Beard emphasizes that treatments are available. None of them guarantees a cure: only four out of Beard's total of thirty cases are deemed "cured," but sixteen are said to have "greatly benefited," and five "slightly benefited" from the treatment (219). The treatment in question is, of course, some form of the general electrization that Beard sponsors.

Significantly, just as Beard overlooks female patients, he ignores psychological therapies. Although the patient's mood may be adversely affected as a consequence of the debilitating nervous exhaustion, Beard refuses to envisage neurasthenia as a condition primarily psychological in origin. Indeed, he moves it quite purposefully from a moral to a medical model. In *American Nervousness* he places the major blame for the high incidence of neurasthenia squarely on the sociological features of modern life: the pressure to overwork that Beard sees as besetting his age could also be subsumed under socie-

tal influences on the individual at a time of economic expansion
when a kind of frenzy to participate in promising developments over-
takes—and overwhelms—some Americans. So it is an excessive zeal
for and commitment to work that may lead to neurasthenia; in other
words, laudable qualities, even strengths, may result in the exhaustion of the nerve force that is at the heart of neurasthenia.

In this line of reasoning, as in some other facets, there is undoubtedly a certain sophistry in Beard's argumentation that arouses the
skepticism—or disbelief—of latter-day readers. Though apparently
specific and learned in his references to many medical phenomena,
on closer analysis Beard often turns out to be quite evasive and slip-
pery. While he concedes that some of his views in the past have been
"mistaken," that the diagnosis was "wrong" in missing "organic disease
of some kind [that was] stealthily eating out the patient's life" (220),
on the whole Beard is remarkably self-assured, not to say dogmatic in
putting forward his theory. He skates over his fundamental lack of convincing proof of the existence of the syndrome on which he elaborates
with such gusto. When he does "admit that this view is speculative," he
asserts his certitude "that it will in time be substantially confirmed by
microscopical and chemical examinations of patients who die in a
neurasthenic condition" (218). The wording here is cautiously tactful:
the patients have not died of neurasthenia but "in a neurasthenic condition," presumably felled by some other disease. In invoking the decisive evidence to be provided in the future by microscopic and chemical postmortem findings, Beard subscribes to the mid-nineteenth-
century faith in pathological anatomy that had already led to such
signal advances in the understanding of disease processes. He therefore capitalizes on knowledge acquired in the past by projecting similar discoveries into the future that will prove his theory. This hopeful
mode of extrapolation is far from the hard-headed, scientific thinking
that Beard's age valued, and in which, by implication, he participates.

The crux of Beard's difficulty lies in his elision of the physical and
the psychological. For Beard's generation, disease could be acknowledged only if it was a well-differentiated clinical entity with distinct
cause, symptomatology, and pathology. Obviously, neurasthenia did
not meet these criteria, so Beard had to work around them as best he
could in order to achieve his aim of getting neurasthenia recognized
as a "morbid condition" (217). He has to resort to a variety of sub-
terfuges to cover the defects of his theory. For example, he fuses
cause and effect inextricably: "Anaemia and neurasthenia may run

into each other, and become so closely interblended that it is oftentimes impossible to determine which was the cause and which was the effect, which was the ruling condition" (217–18). The distinction, according to Beard, is anyway "of little import" (218) as the treatment is the same. This is the most egregious instance of Beard's sustained endeavor to translate the psychological into the physical in the guise of the amorphous category of the absence of nervous force, in order to situate neurasthenia in the favored somatic arena. There must be "slight, undetectable morbid changes in the molecular structure" (218), he maintains—on no more than a hunch. Diagnosis is fuzzy, resting as much on exclusion as on the presence of any of the umpteen putative symptoms of the malady. The fact that neurasthenia "gives *no evidence of anaemia or of any organic disease*" (218; *[sic.]*) could surely have aroused Beard's suspicion of its psychosomatic origin. But this is precisely what he wants to deny. His method is to clothe the psychological in the physical, to convert and assimilate the former to the latter as far as possible because the somatic earned far greater respect at the time than the psychological, which was liable to moral condemnation or to cynical dismissal.

Given the shortcomings and defects of Beard's conceptualization of neurasthenia, how to account for the great vogue for this malady, which escalated to epidemic proportions in the later nineteenth century? A number of reasons for its popularity can be put forward. First of all, it was an essentially benign malady; while it could be diffuse in its manifestations and certainly grievous to the sufferer, it involved no dangerous injury to any of the vital organs. Provided the patient followed a sensible, undemanding, even rather pleasant regimen, centered on a goodly measure of rest and relaxation, recovery was likely, and despite the possibility of relapses, the normal life span was not in jeopardy. Indeed, neurasthenia could even be a protection from other ills, on the analogy of opium consumption—a more than questionable argument. Citing Emerson, Beard likens neurasthenia to a raft that remains afloat whereas a stately ship that strikes a rock goes under. Second, surely as important at the time as the absence of any pathological lesion was the freedom from any suggestion of mental impairment. Quite on the contrary, brain work was listed as a predisposing factor so that to fall prey to neurasthenia could become a source of pride. The young doctor and the busy seventy-year-old lawyer/judge cited by Beard represent models of the type of competent professionals likely to contract the illness out of sheer devotion to their work. Margaret Cleaves fits into the same category. So neurasthenia entailed neither serious physical malfunction nor any emotional imbalance that would have been subject to censure. Moreover, the sufferer was exempt from any personal blame except by virtue of an ardor that proved to exceed his innate nervous force. Finally, what contributed to the widespread acceptance of his new disease entity was Beard's contention that the tendency to neurasthenia was constitutional and hereditary, that is to say, largely beyond the individual's control. He does include some negatives such as "sexual excesses, the abuse of stimulants and narcotics," among the precipitating factors, but these are secondary to "the pressure of bereavement, business and family cares" (218) in the etiology of neurasthenia. It was, therefore, welcome and comforting news to patients such as Margaret Cleaves that their host of disturbing symptoms could be subsumed under a relatively harmless and probably curable heading. The extraordinary success of Beard's questionable disease was assured by its aptitude for enhancing patients' self-esteem, as people who had sickened as a consequence of thoroughly positive traits.

Neurasthenia as a term and a syndrome was readily accepted in psychiatry, as is borne out by its frequent appearance in Krafft-Ebing's *Psychopathia Sexualis* and its ready use by Janet; in fact, it remained in currency well into the twentieth century. Its very vagueness made it, like hysteria, a useful, commodious word to cover a host of poorly understood conditions. It appears in Emil Kraepelin's *Lehrbuch der Psychiatrie für Studierende und Ärzte* (Textbook of Psychiatry for Students and Physicians) in formulations reminiscent of Beard's. As a result of a constitutional disposition ("angeborene Neurasthenie"), precipitated by "Überanstrengung" (overexertion), notably "übermässige Verstandesarbeit" (excessive brain work) and "chronischer Erschöpfung" (chronic fatigue; 65), it may give rise to numerous "nervous" *[sic]* disturbances. As well as this constitutional neurasthenia there is "erworbene Neurasthenie" (acquired neurasthenia). In Kraepelin's nosology the two types do not differ much. But as a psychiatrist Kraepelin put far greater emphasis than Beard on the psychological symptoms such as moodiness, irritability, apathy, and inability to concentrate. In keeping with the trend to a recognition of its essentially psychological nature, neurasthenia migrated in the twentieth century into the successive editions of the American Psychiatric Association's *Diagnostic and Statistical Manual*. But by *DSM-III* (1980) it has been renamed "Dysthymic Disorder (Depressive Neurosis)." Not until *DSM-IV* (1994) does Beard's imaginative neologism fall into abeyance.

∽

Neurasthenia, or Nervous Exhaustion

By George Beard, M.D., Lecturer in Nervous Diseases in the University of New York

I am to speak tonight of a *condition* of the system that is, perhaps, more frequently than any other, in our time at least, the cause and effect of disease.

I refer to *neurasthenia,* or exhaustion of the nervous system.

The morbid condition or state expressed by this term has long been recognized, and, to a certain degree, understood, but the special name *neurasthenia* is now, I believe, for the first time presented to the profession.

It is quite recently, indeed, that the phrase nervous exhaustion has been popularized, at least as a term expressive of a special condition of the system. Prof. Austin Flint, in his Treatise on the "*Principles and Practice of Medicine,*" devotes a brief space to this subject, and acknowledges his indebtedness to Dr. Fordyce Barker for first suggesting the phrase "*nervous asthenia*" as expressive of a special morbid condition. Besides this brief notice of Prof. Flint, this important condition of the nervous system has not, so far as I know, been dignified by a separate heading, or distinct chapter in any of our most approved treatises on the Practice of Medicine, although the general phrase "*nervous exhaustion*" quite frequently occurs in conversation and medical literature, and is now the common property of the profession.

My own attention was called to this morbid condition quite early in my professional life, and in the cultivation of the Department of Neurology and Electro-therapeutics, I have enjoyed excellent opportunities both for the study and the treatment of all the various grades and phases of this frequent malady. As a matter of necessity in describing, recording and studying cases of nervous disease, I have for some time been in the habit of employing the term *neurasthenia* to express the morbid state that is commonly indicated by the indefinite phrase nervous exhaustion.

This nomenclature would seem to be justified by philological analogy, by scientific convenience, and by actual necessity.

The derivation of the term *neurasthenia* is sufficiently obvious. It comes from the Greek νευρον, "a nerve," α, privative, and oθενος, [*sic*] "strength"; and, therefore, being literally interpreted signifies want of strength in the nerve.

The character of this malady, if I be allowed to call it such, may best be understood by comparing and contrasting it with *anaemia*, a condition which has been more thoroughly discussed, and is therefore more vividly appreciated by the profession at large.

Anaemia (derived from α, privative, ν, euphonic, and αιμα, "blood") is to the vascular system what *neurasthenia* is to the nervous. The one means want of *blood;* the other want of *nervous force.*

Both anaemia and neurasthenia may be the *effects* of acute or chronic diseases, and both may be either acute or chronic in their course. Thus neurasthenia may be the effect of wasting fevers, exhausting wounds, parturition, protracted confinement, dyspepsia, phthisis, morbus Brightii and so forth. Anaemia, as is well known, may result from the same diseases.

Both anaemia and neurasthenia may also be the *cause* of chronic and acute diseases. Thus neurasthenia, or nervous exhaustion, may give rise to dyspepsia, headaches, paralysis, insomnia, anaesthesia, neuralgia, rheumatic gout, spermatorrhoea in the male and menstrual irregularities in the female. Anaemia may also be the source of many of these diseases, although perhaps it is more frequently the effect.

Anaemia and neurasthenia may cause each other; anaemia is often the result of neurasthenia, and *vice versa.*

Both anaemia and neurasthenia are most frequently met with in civilized, intellectual communities. They are a part of the compensation for our progress and refinement.

Anaemia and neurasthenia may run into each other, and become so closely interblended that it is often impossible to determine which was the cause and which was the effect, or which is the ruling condition.

Both of these conditions, whether existing separately or in combination, are best treated by some form of constitutional tonics. In anaemia we give those tonics that directly and specially affect the *blood;* in neurasthenia we give those remedies that directly and specially affect the *nervous system.*

In regard to the pathology of neurasthenia we are compelled, in the absence of definite knowledge, to reason from logical probability.

My own view is that the central nervous system becomes dephosphorized, or, perhaps, loses somewhat of its solid constituents; probably also undergoes slight, undetectable morbid changes in its chemical structure, and, as a consequence, becomes more or less impoverished in the quantity and quality of its nervous force.

That molecular disturbance, sufficient to give rise to the symptoms of nervous exhaustion, may take place in the central nervous system, is rendered logically probable by the fact that such changes can be produced artificially, as proved by the researches of du Bois-Reymoud.

We are, I think, driven to accept this view from what we already know of the brain and spinal cord—of their relation to the intelligence and activity, of their intimate chemical structure, of their diverse appearance in health and disease. We know that the intelligence of men and animals is proportioned to the quantity and quality of the cerebral contents, that the proportions of water, of phosphorous, of fat, and of the other solid constituents of the central nervous system vary more or less, with the age and with the intellectual and moral capacity, and that all forms of insanity are dependent on some central morbid condition.

From these established facts we logically conclude that even the slightest and most transient disturbances of the nervous system are the results of correspondingly slight morbid changes of the brain or spinal cord, or of the peripheral nerves.

I admit that this view is speculative, but I feel assured that it will in time be substantially confirmed by microscopical and chemical examinations of those patients who die in a neurasthenic condition.

Neurasthenia may result from any causes that exhaust the nervous system. Hereditary descent terribly predisposes to neurasthenia, just as it predisposes to all forms of nervous derangement. The law of *reversion* is frequently illustrated here, and sick headache, epilepsy or insanity or dyspepsia in the grandfather may skip over a generation and show itself as neurasthenia in the grandchildren. Among the special exciting causes of neurasthenia may be mentioned the pressure of bereavement, business and family cares, parturition and abortion, sexual excesses, the abuse of stimulants and narcotics, and civilized starvation, such as is sometimes observed even among the wealthy order of society, and sudden retirement from business.

The *diagnosis* of the neurasthenic condition is sometimes entirely clear, and again is quite difficult. The diagnosis is obtained partly by the positive symptoms, and partly by exclusion. If a patient complains of general malaise, debility of all the functions, poor appetite, abiding weakness in the back and spine, fugitive neuralgic pains, hysteria, insomnia, hypochondriases, disinclination for consecutive mental labor, severe and weakening attacks of sick headache, and other analogous symptoms, and at the same time gives *no evidence of anaemia or of any organic disease,* we have reason to suspect that the central nervous system is mainly at fault, and that we are dealing with a typical case of neurasthenia. But neurasthenia may be associated with anaemia and with almost every conceivable form of organic disease. In such cases it is sometimes difficult to ascertain whether it is the cause or the effect. The history of the symptoms will help us to decide this question, which is, however, of little import, for in either case the general treatment will be substantially the same.

The *prognosis* in neurasthenia is as various as are the symptoms of the disease. Acute neurasthenia resulting from acute disease usually recovers rapidly; but sometimes becomes chronic, especially when the previous disease has been long and exhausting.

Chronic neurasthenia—of which form I am chiefly speaking—may result in paraplegia, in general paralysis, in neuralgia, in uterine disturbances, in dyspepsia, in chorea, in hypochondriasis, in hysteria, and in actual insanity; or under proper treatment it may go on to perfect recovery.

Chronic neurasthenia sometimes proves directly fatal, without causing any organic disease; but such a termination is not usual. It is, *par excellence,* a chronic condition, and patients afflicted with it may last half a century. We are all of us more or less familiar with such a case. I have a friend who has been afflicted with neurasthenia for more than fifty years, and yet during all this time he has been severely engaged in the complicated duties of a lawyer, judge, and a man of business. There is not an organ in his body that has not suffered from his prolonged neurasthenia; from the time he was fifteen years old until now there has been no day in which he has been free from pain. Even anaemia has supervened, but though the lamp of life has often flickered, yet at the advanced age of seventy it still "holds out to burn."

It is an established fact that opium eaters who are poisoned and weakened by the drug, are comparatively exempt from many other diseases. Opium eaters, I believe, all agree that it is very hard for them to rake cold while under the influence of the evil habit. Just so, neurasthenia seems to protect the system from many acute diseases that so often prove fatal to the hardy and muscular.

Ralph W. Emerson, in one of his essays, quotes an authority who very happily compares a republic to a raft, which never sinks, but always keeps our feet under water, while a monarchy is a stately ship that may at any time strike a rock and go down in an instant.

This comparison just as aptly illustrates the difference between the nervous civilized man and the hardy barbarian. From statistics that I compiled and arranged a few years since, it appears that the expectation of human life or average longevity has at no time been greater than in the present century; that in no other country is it so favorable as in our own, and that no class, on the whole, live longer than our leading brain-workers, who are, of course, peculiarly liable to be affected with chronic neurasthenia.

But though neurasthenic patients live, they "live at a poor, dying rate," and demand and need relief, many of them are very fortunately quite amenable to treatment.

The one principle on which neurasthenia is to be treated is by the concentration of all possible tonic influence on the nervous system—air, sunlight, water, food, rest, diversion, muscular exercise, and the internal administration of those remedies, such as strychnine, phosphorous, arsenic, &c., which directly affect the nervous system.

The nervous tonic which I largely employ in neurasthenia is *general electrization*. In this method of treatment the feet of the patient are placed on a sheet of copper to which the negative pole is attached, while the positive, either a large sponge or the hand of the operator, is applied over the head (the hair being previously moistened), on the back of the neck, down the entire length of the spine, down the arms, over the stomach, the liver, bowels, down the lower extremities—in short, over the entire surface of the body, from the head to the feet, but with special reference to the head and spine.

The evidence that the electric currents when thus applied over the head and spine directly affect the brain and spinal cord, and, to some extent, the nerves that issue from them, are the following:

1. The investigations of Dr. Erb, of Germany.
   By experiments on the cadaver he proved that the galvanic and Faradaic currents directly affected the brain and spinal cord—the galvanic more than the Faradaic.
2. My own repeated observations in cases of myelitis. In some cases of inflammation and even of congestion of the cord, an exceedingly weak current (either galvanic or Faradaic) will sometimes cause the most acutely painful sensations, both in the cord itself, and in the peripheral nerves that go to the viscera and the extremities. On the other hand there are cases of nervous disorder, where

the nerve-centre is in a condition of partial anaesthesia, and consequently bears much stronger applications of electricity than when in a normal condition.

3. The remarkable tonic effects that are produced by applications of electricity over the head, and down the spine, even when the rest of the body is not touched.

These tonic effects of general electrization may be explained in two ways.

First, the electric current may directly improve the quantity and quality of the vital force, in accordance with the theory of the correlation and conservation of forces.

Secondly, the violent and repeated muscular contractions that are produced during the operations of general electrization greatly increase the processes of waste and repair. I once supposed that this passive exercise of the various tissues of the body, internal as well as external, might be the only explanation of the results obtained by general electrization.

That this view was a mistaken one is proved by the fact that these tonic effects are very markedly observed from applications of a mild galvanic current over the surface of the body, even when no muscular contractions are produced.

The power of general electrization to relieve neurasthenia and to cause increase in weight, was illustrated in a very pleasing and satisfactory manner in the case of a young physician whom we have treated during the present autumn. He was twenty-eight years of age, and for a long time subject to severe and repeated attacks of nervous and sick headache. To use his own expression, he had been "living on a lower plane than was normal." Overwork and long confinement had reduced him to a condition of serious exhaustion, and when he called upon us in September he could not walk two miles without fatigue. Although five feet nine and a half inches in height, he weighed but 112 pounds, and for many months there had been no sign of any increase. He had closely studied his own case, had been thoroughly examined, and had tried nearly every form of internal medication.

I began treatment by a mild application of electrization with the Faradaic current. He felt temporarily enlivened and exhilarated, but when he returned two days subsequently, he stated that he felt no special benefit, although he had gained *one half pound in weight.* This change, slight as it was, encouraged him, for it had been months and years even, since he had been able to detect any increase in weight. I may say that he watched and studied his symptoms, and carefully ascertained his weight, from day to day, not as a hypochondriac at all, but as a scientific man, inspired not by any special faith in the remedy, but by an earnest desire to test for himself the tonic effects of general electrization. He continued to increase in weight with remarkable regularity and uniformity, and at the end of three weeks he found that he had increased nine pounds. When I last saw him his weight was 124 pounds. The improvement in his general condition has gone hand in hand with the increase in weight. His appetite is keener, and his digestion much easier. His attacks of headache still annoy him, but his capacity for endurance has been greatly enlarged. Whatever relapses may occur in coming months or years, he feels now that he has at least found a means of relief and permanent benefit.

In this case the applications were made very thoroughly, all over the person from the top of the head to the feet, and with a powerful current. Both the Faradaic and galvanic currents were used, chiefly the Faradaic. It is worthy of remark, also, that this patient always experienced a feeling of temporary enlivenment and exhilaration after each application, and sometimes the headache from which he suffered was driven away in the midst of the treatment.

I may say, also, that when he first came, I prescribed oxide of zinc, by *exclusion*, because he had used nearly every other internal tonic. He took, however, two or three doses of one grain each, for the first day, dropping it entirely as soon as he found that he had increased half a pound in weight.

This case I regarded as preeminently a typical one—a typical illustration of neurasthenia and of the benefit that may be received from general electization.

But sometimes the treatment is protracted for weeks before any decided and permanent benefit is received.

This was well illustrated in the case of a stout, plethoric gentleman, whom we treated for neurasthenia in the summer of 1868. He was treated for several weeks before we could detect or could appreciate any very decided benefit. Finally we alternated the galvanic with the Faradaic current, and succeeded in affording him positive relief from many of the symptoms of nervous exhaustion from which he had suffered for years.

There are cases of neurasthenia that do not yield to general electrization, even after it has been perseveringly employed. These exceptional results may be variously accounted for. It may be that our diagnosis is wrong, and that organic disease of some kind is stealthily eating out the patient's life. It may be that their nervous systems are exhausted beyond restoration. It may be that severer applications and larger perseverance might have resulted in positive benefit.

Dr. Rockwell and myself have records of 30 cases in which nervous exhaustion seemed to be the leading condition. Some of these cases were complicated with hemiplegia, paraplegia, hysteria, hypochondriasis, and so forth; but the majority complained chiefly of, and only sought treatment for, the *general* symptoms of nervous exhaustion, as I have described them. The results of treatment are as follows:—

Cured	4
Greatly benefited	16
Slightly benefited	5
Not perceptibly benefited	5
Total	30

A few of those who who were slightly or greatly benefited have measurably relapsed; but up to the present time the majority, so far as we can learn, have retained or increased the improvement they received. Two or three of the cases that relapsed are now under treatment.

In the limited time allowed me on this occasion it has been manifestly impossible to do anything more than to present the outlines of so important a subject as neurasthenia. I have, therefore, not aimed to be exhaustive, but only to be *suggestive.*

The principles on which I mainly insist and to which I shall call special attention, are briefly these:—

1. The term neurasthenia, as expressive of a very important and increasingly frequent condition of the system, is eminently justified by philological analogy, by convenience and by necessity.
2. The one principle on which this morbid condition should be treated, is by the employment, either separately or together, of constitutional tonics, that specially affect the nervous system.
3. Among the various internal and external tonic remedies for neurasthenia, general electrization is oftentimes preëminent. The superiority of general electrization in cases where internal medication has failed, is apparent in the ease and rapidity with which it increases the appetite, promotes sleep, and develops the size and weight of the muscles—thus preparing the way for the *digestion of food,* which is itself one of the very best of tonics; for *rest,* which is

really food for the nerves; for muscular exercise, which, in its turn, prepares the way for air and sunlight.

In this capacity of general electrization for marshalling to its aid other tonic influences, lies, I think, the secret of its power, perhaps the best interpretation of its success.

NOTES

1. The very existence of these recent reprints testifies to the lasting life of "neuras-thenia."

2. Arthur Wrobelin, ed., *Pseudo-Science and Society in Nineteenth-Century America* (Lexington: University of Kentucky Press, 1987), 46–73.

3. Lynn Gamwell and Nancy Tooms, *Madness in America: Cultural and Medical Perceptions of Illness Before 1914,* (Ithaca and London: Cornell University Press, 1995), 139.

4. Erb, Wilhelm, *Handbuch der Elektrotherapie.* Leipzig: Verlag von F. C. W. Vogel, 1882.

2

Richard von Krafft-Ebing

FROM *PSYCHOPATHIA SEXUALIS* (1886)

PSYCHOPATHIA SEXUALIS CAUSED NOT JUST A SENSATION BUT A VERITAble scandal on its appearance in 1886. At that time overt discussion of sexuality was absolutely prohibited in polite society, although this does not mean that there was no covert awareness of the power of the sexual drive, as many literary works testify. Consciousness of sexual feelings, particularly removed to fictitious characters, was, however, a very different matter from a direct articulation of a subject simply considered unfit to be acknowledged, let alone voiced. Even the reading of novels was regarded as unsuitable for unmarried women because of the potentially corrupting influence that sexual knowledge might exert. Sexuality was silently and grudgingly recognized as an element of human life, but the attempt to repress or indeed to deny its importance was strenuously maintained. In short, sex was taboo.

Krafft-Ebing (1840–1902) acknowledges the innovative, not to say revolutionary nature of his endeavor when he describes it at the beginning of his preface as exploring a still almost virginal area of scientific knowledge (iii; "ein noch nahezu jungfräulicher wissenschaftlicher Boden"). The metaphor "virginal" seems a somewhat comical pun in this context. What made Krafft-Ebing's work even more shocking was his concentration not merely on sexuality but on the incomparably more dangerous topic of sexual *deviations*. On the title page of his treatise he declares his specific concern with "Conträren Sexualempfindungen" (contrary, that is, abnormal sexual feelings). While Krafft-Ebing is reputed to have coined the terms *sadism* and *masochism*, he hardly ever uses such words as *homosexuality, homoeroticism,* or *inversion,* although he does cover such sexual activity. He has recourse in his preface to numerous metaphoric phrases to characterize his focus on the pathological manifestations of sexuality: the "Nachtseite des Lebens" (v; the night side of life), its "Kehrseite" (v; reverse side), its "tiefe Schatten" (iv; dark shadows), its "Elend" (v; misery), in contrast to "das glänzende Götterbild des Dichters" (v; the poet's glowing divine image). By using such lofty, pseudopoetic phrases, Krafft-Ebing was perhaps trying to cushion the impact of his sordid subject matter. This may also account for his use of such commonplace, quite innocuous words as *peculiar* and *quirky* to describe even the weirder of the figures he delineates. Absolutely nonjudgmental, he resorts to understatement to play down the bizarre and the offensive.

This pessimistic acknowledgment of the existence of sexual deviations is counteracted by Krafft-Ebing's confidence that the problem he outlines can be solved with the help of science and especially of medicine (v; "unter Mithilfe der Naturwissenschaft und speziell der Medicin"). In this great faith in science Krafft-Ebing partakes of the beliefs of his age. His quest for truth (v; "Forschung nach Wahrheit") has to take as its starting point an open confrontation of the wounds, the festering sores, the rotten spots that the man of science must face without fear. Again, the metaphors he invokes are striking. To buttress the significance of his research Krafft-Ebing insists that hitherto there had been little awareness of the enormous importance of sexuality in both individual and social life in many areas: feelings, thoughts, and actions.

This emphasis on the scientific purpose of *Psychopathia Sexualis* was also likely motivated by the hope of defusing the anticipated opposition. So Krafft-Ebing explicitly states in his preface that sale of the book is to be rigidly restricted solely to doctors and lawyers. As a further part of his endeavor to exclude lay readers he intersperses technical and Latin phrases, sometimes entire sentences, so as to make his work less widely accessible since Latin was the language of the learned, much used especially in Europe among medical men to withhold information from their patients—and incidentally to enable them to discuss patients' symptoms and diseases in their presence under the cover of secrecy. Despite these defensive measures, Krafft-Ebing encountered widespread censure and opprobrium. He had, for instance, to dissuade the British Medical Psychological Association from cancelling his membership. The crux of the problem lay in the difficulty of determining the fine line between scientific vulgarization and pornography. Although Krafft-Ebing presents his work as a serious contribution to scholarly knowledge of human behavior, it was suspected of being the product of a prurient voyeuristic curiosity.

Notwithstanding the furor that met *Psychopathia Sexualis,* it also enjoyed considerable success, albeit a *succès de scandale.* The first slen-

der edition was quickly followed by expanded versions, enriched by
the addition of numerous further cases. The third edition of 1888
(the basis for this translation) was already two-thirds longer than the
original one. By the twelfth edition, from which the first English
translation was made in 1926, the cases amounted to 238. Some of
these cases are cited from previously published journal articles by
others, but the majority draw on Krafft-Ebing's own observations.
The appropriation of others' cases (with due acknowledgment) was
a not uncommon practice in the nineteenth century, when journals
were often not easily available, so that instead of a brief reference, as
became customary with the greater spread of information, an entire
case (or its pertinent section) would be reprinted. A prime example
of this habit is found in Daniel Hack Tuke's *Influence of the Mind upon
the Body* (1872), in which Tuke freely mingles his experiences of the
phenomenon he is studying with those of others. Isolated instances
of behavior that departed from the norm were, however, if scattered
in journals, far less offensive than *Psychopathia Sexualis* precisely
because these incidents were seen as anomalies worthy of reporting
as *exceptions* whereas in his work Krafft-Ebing, through his ever growing collection of similar cases, projects a picture of a diffused pattern
of deviant behavior. It is the cumulative impact of his multiple cases
that stirred such indignation on account of the underlying implication of the degeneracy of human nature.

Krafft-Ebing was particularly well placed to observe alienating
behavior since he was professor of forensic psychiatry at the University of Graz in Upper Austria. One of his routine obligations in that
position was to examine severe cases of sexual abnormality brought
before the courts. His keen interest in criminal law is reflected in
the appendixes to his work of clauses from the Austrian penal code
about topics such as necrophilia, incest, and immoral conduct toward
minors, notably seduction. He also at times records the legal outcome of his cases, such as commitment to an insane asylum, light sentence, suspension of proceedings, or execution. In marked contrast
to this elaboration of the legal conclusions, Krafft-Ebing, perhaps
because he was a forensic specialist, shows virtually no interest in therapeutic possibilities, even in patients who consult him about their
sexual problems outside a legal framework. By and large he envisages
his cases as hopelessly beyond remedy so that he very rarely offers
sociomedical advice about treatment or the prospect of improvement.
Nonetheless, a few cases turn out well; in others he comments with a
certain amount of sympathy on the ways in which the delinquent's

family coped with an embarrassing situation, especially among members of the upper class, from whom several of his cases originated.

Instead of the therapeutic means that preoccupied the practitioners of hypnosis and suggestion, Krafft-Ebing's primary aim is that of classification. He begins his opus by setting up sundry categories of what he calls "Neuro- and Psycho-Pathology" in a complex "Schema of Sexual Neuroses" that are divided into "Peripheral Neuroses," which are in turn subdivided into "Sensory," "Secretory," "Motor," and "Spinal Neuroses." This last category is still further subdivided into, on the one hand, "Affections of the Erection Center," which comprise "Irritation," "Paralysis," "Inhibition," and "Irritable Weakness," and, on the other hand, "Affections of the Ejaculatory Center," namely, "Abnormal Ease in Ejaculation" and "Abnormal Dfficulty in Ejaculation." The later editions show refinement of these basic categories as well as enrichment through more exemplary cases.

Krafft-Ebing clearly articulates his purpose as the recognition of the pathological manifestations of sexual life (iv; "Kenntnisnahme der pathologischen Erscheinungen des Sexuallebens und der Versuch ihrer Zurückführung auf gesetzmässige Bedingungen") and the attempt to trace them back to circumstances governed by determinable laws. This concept of "determinable laws" distinctly signals Krafft-Ebing's endeavor to import into psychiatry the stringent methods that governed the biological sciences. He concedes that his chosen task is difficult and incomplete despite many years of collecting relevant cases. He also maintains that this task can be undertaken only by a forensic physician (iv; "Gerichtsarzt") who has direct access to the necessary evidence. Krafft-Ebing's fundamental aim is thus one of systematization as the essential preliminary step toward an understanding of the perplexities of deviations in human sexual behavior. In this emphasis on classification *Psychopathia Sexualis* stands in the wake of Emil Kraepelin's landmark *Lehrbuch der Psychiatrie* (Textbook of Psychiatry), which was first published in 1883 and also ran into many successive editions. Kraepelin and Krafft-Ebing are obvious forerunners of the twentieth-century *Diagnostic and Statistical Manual* of the American Psychiatric Association; as its predecessors it has run into multiple editions, each more voluminous than the previous one and each encompassing an ever growing number of differentiated syndromes.

Krafft-Ebing's classificatory aim also determines the actual manner in which he presents his cases. Often he writes in note form, as in clinical records, using incomplete sentences and abrupt phrases. His

style can best be described as essentially laconic, devoid of any literary pretensions, dry and legalistic, as if to underscore his own distance and detachment from the phenomena he presents. His slant
toward the legal aspects fosters the utmost factuality. However, the
price paid for this preference for precision is an attenuation of the
human and social texture of the figures on whom he reports. Again
in conformity with nineteenth-century usage, he provides the barest
of personal information: merely an initial (obviously to protect
anonymity), age, occupation, sometimes social standing, as when he
refers to one case as a "Dame" (lady), a term that posits a higher social
standing than the normative "Frau" (woman). At times they are
almost depersonalized into exemplars of a typology rather than
rounded individuals; they are dominated by their quirkiness, which
overrides all other characteristics. Yet precisely because of their
bizarre fixations, such as a fetish for servants' waxed boots, they are
unforgettable. They come to life best when Krafft-Ebing cites their
own statements, either in quotes or in indirect discourse. This is a tactic to which he resorts at the most outrageous points such as that of
the man with religious mania who impregnates his daughter.

   In order to fulfil his primary purpose of classification Krafft-Ebing
had to adduce a large number of cases so as to survey the field. Some
of his case histories are therefore quite cursory, introduced to supplement and support the categories he is seeking to establish. A few of the
accounts are relatively more extensive, covering several years in the
development of the subject's delinquency. Generally, however, Krafft-
Ebing uses the customary nineteenth-century method of accumulation of evidence by accretion. Such a procedure devolved from the
discovery by the French scientist Pierre Louis (1787–1882) of the
importance and usefulness of statistics in epidemiology. Because of his
firm focus on the overall schema Krafft-Ebing pays scant attention to
the individuality of the cases except insofar as they illustrate his thesis.
He spans the entire social spectrum from well-to-do aristocrats to day
laborers, thereby demonstrating the ubiquity of the deviations he
describes. The majority of his subjects are male, perhaps because of his
exploration of the problems associated with ejaculation as well as the
preponderance of males among those breaking the law. He accepts
without question the possibility of hysteria in males, which was still
much disputed at the time. Among the female patients delinquency is
frequently connected to the timing of menstruation or menopause.

   Given the scantness of the personal information about his patients,
it is remarkable just how much attention Krafft-Ebing devotes to their

heredity. Almost invariably he records whether a patient has either a tainted or a hitherto healthy family. Among the hereditary tarnishes he includes a diversity of factors such as tuberculosis, seizures, alcoholism, and insanity. The line of demarcation between physical and mental afflictions was in many instances not yet well understood at the time; epilepsy, for example, was long regarded as an exclusively mental illness. The overriding importance Krafft-Ebing attaches to heredity reflects the predominant views of the latter part of the nineteenth century (see introduction). The tendency to degeneration passes exponentially from generation to generation, surfacing in siblings who are frequently cited as adjunct evidence of the patient's condition. The notion of degeneracy is supported too by Krafft-Ebing's categoric contention that the sexual functioning of civilized people is very frequently abnormal (22; "Überaus häufig erweisen sich bei dem Culturmenschen die sexuellen Funktionen abnorm").

Hereditary degeneracy was also a favored theme in the literature of the period. It is prominent in such plays as Ibsen's *Ghosts* (1881) and Strindberg's *Miss Julie* (1888). Heredity structures the generational novel popular in the late nineteenth and early twentieth century. Contemporaneous to *Psychopathia Sexualis,* Émile Zola's *Rougon-Macquart* is almost a fictionalized companion to Krafft-Ebing's theories in their mutual attempt systematically to explore the ravages of hereditary degeneracy (see introduction).

For Krafft-Ebing, as for Zola, the roots of degeneracy are primarily physical, in the diseases, destructive inclinations, and other constitutional weaknesses transmitted within families. Such an emphasis on somatic causes is in consonance with the nineteenth century's strong commitment to the physical interpretation of human life following the immense progress made in the latter two-thirds of that century in the medical understanding of the body's disease mechanisms through the discovery of germs and the invention of instruments from the stethoscope in the 1830s to x-rays in 1895 that allowed insight into the body's recesses. So the nineteenth century developed a high degree of confidence in its capacity to master the physical processes of human life. Despite his therapeutic pessimism, or at least indifference, Krafft-Ebing seems to subscribe to this confidence, as to many other prevailing beliefs of his time, by indicating that classification is a first step toward further advances. So in case 51, the man who dies of tuberculosis in the insane asylum, he has an autopsy of the brain performed in an attempt to find the pathological lesions that might account for his mental aberrations.

Krafft-Ebing also conformed to the tendencies of his time in his elevation of the somatic over the psychological (see introduction). For instance, in his consideration of affectations of the erection and the ejaculatory centers, he is more intent on such physical causes as irritation, paralysis, and weakness than on the psychological element of inhibition. Similarly, in women strange behavior is attributed to the onset of menstruation or to menopause, while in men it is repeatedly ascribed to excessive masturbation. Although Krafft-Ebing occasionally refers to the role of the psyche in sexual problems, he does not pursue this line of thought at all. On the contrary, once more in accordance with the trends of his age, he almost invariably prefers to envisage these difficulties as devolving from bodily states. So he appears to believe that the actual size of the genitals is decisive for sexual functioning.

Another striking consequence of the low esteem of psychology is apparent in *Psychopathia Sexualis* in the consistent, marked disregard for the possible presence of interpersonal and, to a somewhat lesser extent, of intrapsychic conflicts in the etiology of sexual pathologies (see introduction). The family problems and tensions that so often prove to be at the core of mental disorders in Freud's perceptions of neuroses are of absolutely no interest to Krafft-Ebing. He shows no concern whatsoever for family relationships, recording instead primarily physical histories.

Despite these limitations, Krafft-Ebing was unquestionably a pioneer in research into sexuality. *Psychopathia Sexualis* stimulated subsequent work in the field such as the journal founded in 1899 by Magnus Hirschfeld, the *Jahrbuch für sexuelle Zwischenstufen* (Journal for Sexual Anomalies). But its evident scholarly intent did not protect any type of sex research from continuing suspicion and censure. The seven-volume study by the English Havelock Ellis (1850–1939), published between 1897 and 1928, was, as was *Psychopathia Sexualis,* legally available only to the medical profession, even though it dealt with the psychology of sex, including women's rights and the need for sexual education, not with the perversions that formed Krafft-Ebing's material.

Krafft-Ebing also totally eschews any mention of normal sexuality. He tacitly assumes heterosexual intercourse and procreation as intrinsic to the marital state, but he focuses exclusively on deviations from this norm. Although he insists on the frequency of such deviations, he separates them sharply from normal behavior. While his exploration of aberrations horrified his contemporaries, at least they did not touch the normal majority personally since the conditions outlined by Krafft-Ebing were presented as clearly pathological. Shocking though these cases were, ultimately they were less threatening than the theories expounded by Freud at the turn of the century, for Freud perceived sexuality is a **normal** part of ordinary human life; he recognized sexual feelings and drives as naturally innate to the healthy, and not limited solely to deviants. What is more, such feelings and drives were experienced by women (and indeed children) as well as by men. In many of his case histories he uncovered the tensions, conflicts, temptations, traumas, and unfaithfulness concealed beneath the apparently respectable facade of decent bourgeois families. Such discussion of sexuality as intrinsic, even central to human existence is in sharp contrast to that of Krafft-Ebing, who disregarded all but the abnormal. The "contrary sexual feelings" of criminals and the insane could more easily be pushed aside as a category unto themselves, removed from the conduct of proper, ordinary people. Freud's theses struck at the heart of Victorian prudery by illustrating the pervasiveness of sexuality, a concept radically more disturbing than Krafft-Ebing's marginalized exceptions.

Out of the seventy-five cases presented in the third edition of *Psychopathia Sexualis* I have chosen to translate just fifteen. Two principles govern my selection: to give a representative sample of the types of aberration recorded by Krafft-Ebing, and to include some of the cases (e.g., 2, 4, 7, 20, 48, and 51) that he singled out as of particular importance. I have, of course, used only cases that draw directly on the author's own observations, not those cited from others.

∽

GENERAL (NEURO- AND PSYCHO-) PATHOLOGY

Very commonly the sexual functions of civilized people turn out to be abnormal. This fact can be explained partly through the frequent misuse of the generative organ, and partly through the circumstance that such functional anomalies are often signs of a predominantly pathological disposition of the central nervous system ("signs of functional degeneration").

But since the generative organs have a significant functional relationship to the entire nervous system in both its psychological and somatic aspects, the frequency of general neuroses as well as psychoses stemming from sexual (functional or organic) disturbances is understandable.

Schema of Sexual Neuroses.

I. Peripheral Neuroses.

1) Sensory

a) Anesthesia. b) Hyperasthesia. c) Neuralgia.

2) Secretory

a) Aspermia. b) Polyspermia.

3) Motor

a) Pollutions (spasms). b) Spermatorrhea (paralysis).

4) Spinal Neuroses.

1) Affectations of the Erection Center.

a) *Irritation* (priapism) arises from reflex reaction to peripheral sensory irritations (e.g. gonorrhea), directly through irritation of the conduits from the brain to the erection center (spinal disease in the lower cervical or upper dorsal regions) or of the center itself (certain poisons) or through psychological disturbances.

In the latter case there is satyriasis, that is, abnormally lengthy duration of the erection with sexual libido. In purely reflex or directly organic irritation, the libido may be absent and the priasmus itself associated with feelings of aversion.

b) *Paralysis* through destruction of the center or of the conduits (nervi erigentes) in diseases of the spinal cord (paralytic impotence).

A milder form of this is lessened excitability of the center as a result of its having been overexcited (sexual excesses, especially onanism) or intoxication with alcohol, bromides, etc. It may be connected with cerebral anesthesia, often also with anesthesia of the outer genitalia. More frequently in these cases there is cerebral hyperasthesia (increased sexual libido, lustfulness).

A special form of reduced excitability is represented by those cases in which the center is responsive only to certain stimuli and able to produce an erection. Thus there are men who do not derive the necessary momentum from sexual contact with their virtuous wife, but the momentum does arise if the act takes place with a prostitute or is attempted in the form of an unnatural sexual action. Insofar as psychological stimuli come into play here, they can even be inadequate (see paresthesia and perversion of sexual activity).

c) *Inhibition.* The erection center can become unable to function through cerebral influences emanating from the brain. This inhibiting influence is either an emotional process (revulsion, fear of infection) or the outcome of a concept of insufficient potency. In the first category there are many men who have an insuperable aversion to women, or fear of infection, or who are locked into perverse sexual feelings; in the latter category there are also many neuropaths (neurotics, hypochondriacs), often, too, many weakened in their potency (onanists) who have reason to distrust or think they have reason to distrust their potency. The relevant psychic process acts as a belief in their inhibition, and renders the act with the person of the opposite sex temporarily or permanently impossible.

d) *Irritable Weakness.* Here there is abnormal impressionability but rapid decline of the center's energy. It may be a matter of the functional disturbance of the center itself or weakness of innervation in the nervi erigentes or weakness of the erector penis muscles. As a transition to the following anomalies those cases must be mentioned where the erection is inadequate owing to abnormally early ejaculation.

2) Affectations of the Ejaculatory Center

a) *Abnormal Ease of Ejaculation* through lack of cerebral inhibition as a consequence of great psychic excitement, or through the center's irritable weakness. In this case according to the circumstances simply the thought of a lascivious situation suffices to activate the center (high degrees of spinal neurasthenia, mostly as a result of sexual misuse). Hyperasthesia of the urethra is a third possibility that causes an immediate and violent reflex action of the emerging sperm. In such cases merely the approach to the female genitalia may suffice to trigger the ejaculation (ante portam [before the door]).

If hyperasthesia of the urethra is the cause, the ejaculation can occur with a sensation of pain instead of pleasure. In almost all cases of hyperasthesia of the urethra there is also a simultaneous irritable weakness of the center. Both these functional disturbances are important for the production of pollution by night and day.

The accompanying feeling of pleasure may be pathologically lacking. This occurs in men and women with a defect (anesthesia, aspermia?), and also as a consequence of disease (neurasthenia, hysteria), or (in prostitutes) as a result of over-stimulation and the blunting arising from it. The degree of the psychic and motor excitement accompanying the sexual act is connected to the power of the sensation of pleasure. In pathological circumstances pleasure may be so great that the movements of coitus attain a convulsive character independent of the will, or even develop into general convulsions.

b) *Abnormal Difficulty of Ejaculation.* It is conditioned by inexcitability of the center (absence of libido, paralysis of the center, organically through diseases of the brain or the spinal cord, functionally through sexual misuse, marasmus [wasting], diabetes, addiction to morphine), mostly associated with anesthesia of the genitalia and paralysis of the erection center. Or it is a consequence of a lesion of the reflex arc or of peripheral anesthesia (of the urethra) or of aspermia. Ejaculation occurs not at all in the course of the sexual act or only later in the form of pollution.

PARADOXIA: SEXUAL URGE BEYOND THE TIME OF ANATOMICAL AND PHYSIOLOGICAL PROCESSES

Case 2. Mr. X., eighty, of high social standing, from a family with a hereditary taint, always sexually very needy, a cynic, with an abnormal, violent temperament, even in his youth, according to his own confession, preferred masturbation over coitus, but never showed signs of aberrant sexuality, had mistresses, and fathered a child with one of them, married at age forty-eight out of inclination, fathered a further six children, never gave his wife cause for complaint during their marriage. I could ascertain only incompletely the situation in his family. What is certain is that his brother was suspected of homosexuality, and that a nephew went insane as a result of excessive masturbation.

Over the years the patient's peculiar, violent temperament has grown more extreme. He has become exceedingly suspicious; minor opposition to his wishes arouses disproportionate feelings amounting to attacks of anger in which he even raises his hand against his wife.

For the past year there have been clear signs of incipient senile dementia. The patient has become forgetful, he places past events in incorrect locations, and is not properly oriented temporally. For the past fourteen months the old man's manifest love for certain male servants, particularly for a gardener lad, has become noticeable. Otherwise gruff and distanced toward his inferiors, he heaps privileges and favors on this favorite, and orders his family and domestic staff to show him the greatest respect. The old man awaits the hours of their meetings with real fervor. He sends his family away in order to be alone with his favorite, remains closeted with him for hours, and when the doors are opened again, is found on his bed, totally exhausted. Apart from this lover, the patient has episodic relations with other servants. It has been established that he entices them, demands kisses from them, is exhibitionistic, lets his genitalia be groped, and instigates mutual masturbation. This behavior has caused utter demoralization. The family is powerless, for every protest evokes attacks of anger including threats against his relatives. The patient is completely lacking in insight for his sexually perverse conduct so that a declaration of incompetence and removal to an asylum is the only remaining solution for this disconsolate, highly respected family.

No erotic feeling toward the opposite sex can be noted, although the patient still shares a bedroom with his wife. What is remarkable in regard to this unfortunate man's perverse sexuality and his degraded moral sense is the fact that he asks his daughter-in-law's women servants whether she has a lover.

Aneasthesia sexualis

Case 4. P., thirty-six, day laborer, was admitted to my clinic at the beginning of November because of spastic spinal paralysis. He maintains that he comes from a healthy family. A stutterer since his youth. Cranium microcephalic. Patient somewhat imbecilic. He has never been sociable, had never felt a sexual impulse. The sight of a woman had never held any attraction for him. Never had he felt a masturbatory urge. Frequent erections, but only in the morning on awaking with a full bladder and without a trace of sexual impulse. Pollutions very rare, about once a year, in his sleep, and mostly associated with dreams of contact with a female individual. A decidedly erotic content was not, however, characteristic of these dreams or of his dreams altogether. A real sense of desire did not accompany the act of pollution. The patient is not aware of this absence of sexual feelings. He gave the assurance that his thirty-four-year-old brother was sexually the same as he, and thinks it likely of a twenty-one-year-old sister. A younger brother is said to be sexually normal. Examination of the patient's genitalia revealed nothing abnormal except phimosis [narrowness of the opening of the prepuce, preventing its being drawn back over the glans].

Hyperaesthesia

Case 6. For the past three years the widely respected, married farmer D., thirty-five years old, had shown ever more frequent and vehement states of sexual excitement that had in the past year heightened into veritable paroxysms of satyriasis. No hereditary or other organic cause could be found.

At times of greater sexual excitement he had to have intercourse ten to fifteen times in twenty-four hours without deriving any satisfaction.

Gradually he developed a state of general nervous irritation with great irritability of temperament rising to pathological outbreaks of anger and the urge to alcoholic excesses that brought on symptoms of alcoholism. His attacks of satyriasis reached such a pitch that the patient's consciousness was affected and he let himself yield blindly to the urge of sexual acts. So he demanded that his wife should engage in intercourse with other men or animals in his presence and *praesentibus filiabus* [with his son present] because this gave him enhanced pleasure! He had no memory of the happenings at the climax of these attacks, in which his extreme irritability led to outbreaks of anger. D. himself thought that he had had moments in which he was no longer in command of his senses, and, lacking satisfaction from his wife, had had to go for the nearest available female. After a violent change of mood these episodes of sexual excitement suddenly dissipated.

Case 7. On 29 May 1882 F, twenty-three, single, a cobbler, was admitted to the hospital. His father had a vicious temper, his mother was a neuropath, and her brother was insane.

The patient had never before been seriously sick, does not drink, but had always been sexually very needy. Five days ago he had become acutely sick mentally. In broad daylight and in the presence of witnesses he attempted two crimes, under arrest uttered obscenities in a delirium, masturbated endlessly, on the third day fell into an

angered frenzy, and on his admission to hospital presented the picture of a serious, acute delirium with violently irritated movements
and fever. Through treatment with ergotaminine a cure was effected.

On 5 January 1888 a second admission to hospital in angered
frenzy. On the fourth, he had become morose, irritable, weepy,
unable to sleep, then after fruitless attacks on women he had suffered
increasingly angry excitement.

On the sixth, his condition worsened to violent acute delirium
(serious disturbances of consciousness, ejaculations, gnashing of his
teeth, grimaces among other motor symptoms of irritation, temperature up to 40.7). Compulsive masturbation. Recovery as a result of
energetic treatment with ergotaminine until 11 January.

On recovery the patient gives interesting information about the
cause of his illness.

Always very needy sexually. First coitus at age sixteen. Abstinence
caused headaches, great mental irritability, fatigue, decline of his
desire to work, insomnia. Since he rarely had opportunity to satisfy
his needs out in the country, he resorted to masturbation. He had to
masturbate once or twice a day.

In the past two months no coitus. Increasing sexual arousal, could
think only of means to satisfy the urge. Masturbation was not enough
to banish the complaints that became ever more insistent as a result
of abstinence. In the preceding days strong urge to coitus, growing
insomnia and irritability. Only fragmentary memories at the height
of the illness. Patient recovered in December, a very decent human
being. He perceives his uncontrollable urge as decidedly pathological and has fears for the future.

Case 9. Mrs. V. has since her earliest youth suffered from nympho-
mania. From a good family, well educated, agreeable, moral to the
point of blushing, she was already as a young girl the terror of her
family. As soon as she was left alone with a person of the opposite sex,
irrespective whether he was a child, a grown man, or an old man, ugly
or handsome, she would immediately strip and voraciously demand
satisfaction of her sexual urges, even resorting to physical assault. An
attempt was made to cure her through marriage. She loved her husband madly, but besides him she could not help desiring coitus with
every other man she could encounter alone, servants, workmen, students, etc.

Nothing could cure her of this urge, even when she was a grandmother. One day she enticed a twelve-year-old boy into her room, and
wanted to rape him. The boy fought her off and escaped. She was

roundly reproved by his brother. Everything was forgiven. She was put into a convent. There she was a model of morality, not guilty of the slightest infraction. As soon as she came out, she again began her scandalous behavior. The family banished her, depriving her of a small pension. Through the work of her own hands she earned the necessary minimum to enable her to buy lovers. No one who saw this neatly dressed old lady with good manners and affable character could suspect how ruthless and sexually needy she still was at the age of sixty-five. On 17 January 1854 her family, in despair at new scandals, committed her to an insane asylum.

She lived there until 17 May 1858 when she succumbed to a cerebral apoplexy in her seventy-third year. Her behavior under supervision in the asylum was perfect. Left to herself and in favorable circumstances, her sexual urges became manifest until shortly before her death. Apart from this, observation by psychiatrists over four years never yielded any sign of mental abnormality.

Perversion of the Sexual Urge

Case 15. The girl slasher of Augsburg. Bartle, a wine merchant, had strong sexual urges at fourteen already, but a decisive aversion to satisfying them through coitus with women. At that time already he had the idea of slashing girls as a means to attain sexual satisfaction. He did not do so, however, out of lack of opportunity and courage.

He disdained masturbation; every now and then he had pollutions with erotic dreams of slashed girls.

At age nineteen he slashed a girl for the first time. With this action he had an ejaculation and the utmost sensual pleasure. Thereafter the impulse became ever more powerful. He chose only young and pretty girls, and asked them beforehand whether they were still single. Sometimes ejaculation and sexual satisfaction occurred, but only when he could see that he had really injured the girl. After the attack he always felt exhausted and sick as well as tortured by a bad conscience. Up to the age of thirty-two he wounded girls by slashing, but always took care not to inflict dangerous wounds on the girls. From then until the age of thirty-six he was able to control his urge. Then he tried to find satisfaction merely by pressing on a girl's arm or neck, but he achieved thereby only an erection, not an ejaculation. Then he tried to stab the girl with the knife left in the slash wound, but that did not suffice either. Finally he stabbed with the open knife and had complete success as he imagined that a stabbed girl bled more and had more pain than a slashed one. In his thirty-seventh year he was caught and arrested. At his home a lot of daggers and knives were found. He maintained that the mere sight of these weapons, and even more touching them, had given him feelings of sexual pleasure and strong excitement.

In total, according to his own confession he had injured fifty girls.

His outer appearance was rather pleasant. He lived in very good circumstances, was a peculiar person, shy of people.

Active and Passive Flagellation

Case 20. Z., a law student, twenty years old, comes from a tainted family. His sister was mentally ill, his brother suffered from *Hysteria virilis* [male hysteria]. The patient has been strange ever since childhood, has frequent hypochondriac attacks of depression, *Taed. vitae* [dejection], feels himself to be at a disadvantage. At a consultation for "mental suffering" I find a highly eccentric, introverted person with symptoms of neurasthenia and hypochondria. The suspicion of masturbation is confirmed. The patient gives interesting information about his *Vita sexualis* [sexual life]. At the age of ten he was strongly attracted by a comrade's foot. At fourteen he had begun to be entranced by women's feet. It gave him great pleasure to bask in the sight of them. At fourteen he began to masturbate while thinking of a woman's pretty foot. From then on he took delight in the feet of his sister who was three years older than he. The feet of other ladies, provided they were attractive, aroused him sexually. Only feet interested him in women. The thought of sexual intercourse with a woman disgusted him. He has never tried coitus. From the age of twelve onward he never again felt interest in a man's feet. The way in which a female foot is clothed is a matter of indifference to him; what is decisive is that the personality strike him as attractive. The thought of enjoying prostitutes' feet repels him. He has for years been in love with his sister's feet. If he merely catches a glimpse of her shoes, his sensuality is greatly stimulated. A kiss or an embrace from his sister does not have the same effect. His utmost aspiration is to embrace and kiss an attractive woman's foot. Then, with lively feelings of desire, he ejaculates. He has often felt the urge to touch his genitals with his sister's shoe, but so far he has managed to control this urge, especially as he has in the past two years ejaculated at the mere sight of her foot (as a result of irritated genital weakness). From his relatives we learn that the patient has an absurd admiration for his sister's feet so that she avoids him and takes care to conceal her feet from the patient. The patient regards his perverse sexual urge as pathological, and is embarrased by the fact that his dirty fantasies are directed precisely at his sister's feet. To the best of his ability he shuns the opportunity to help himself out by masturbation in which, as in his dream pollutions, women's feet float in his fantasy. If the urge grows too strong, he cannot resist partaking of the sight of his sister's feet. Immediately after ejaculation he feels great annoyance at having been weak again. His predilection for his sister's feet has cost him countless sleepless nights. He often wonders whether he can still like his sister. Although he finds it right that she hides her feet from him, he is often very irritated at the fact that he thereby forfeits his pollutions. The patient emphasizes that he is otherwise honest, as is confirmed by his relatives.

Transitional Forms to Acquired Contrary Sexual Feelings

Case 48. Mr. von X., of high social standing, a Russian, twenty-eight years old, comes to see me one day in desperation in order to consult me on the perversion of his *Vita sexualis* [sexual life] that has made his life seem almost intolerable to him and that had several times already brought him to the verge of suicide.

The patient comes from a family with a history of frequent neuroses and psychoses. On his father's side early incestuous relationships had occurred for three generations. His father is said to be healthy and to have a good marriage. Yet the son notices his father's predilection for beautiful servants. His mother's family is portrayed as full of bizarre characters. His mother's father and grandfather died melancholy, and her sister was insane. A daughter of the grandfather's brother was hysterical and nymphomanic. Of his mother's twelve siblings only three married. Among these one brother was sexually contrary and always nervously ill as a result of excessive masturbation. The patient's mother was bigoted, of limited intelligence, nervous, irritable, and with a tendency to melancholia.

The patient has two siblings—a neuropathic, often melancholy brother who, though adult, had never shown signs of sexual impulses, and a sister, an acknowledged beauty, adored by all men.

This lady is married but childless, allegedly on account of her husband's impotence. She has always been cold in response to men's adoration, but is entranced by female beauty and virtually in love with certain of her women friends.

In regard to his own personality the patient reports that at age 4 already he had dreamt of riding servants with beautifully waxed boots. As an adult too he had never dreamt of a woman. His nightly pollutions were always provoked by "boot dreams."

From his fourth year onward he had felt a special inclination toward men, or more precisely to lackeys who wore beautifully waxed boots. At first they were merely attractive to him; with the development of his sexuality, the sight of tnem provoked strong erections and lustful excitement. Only in servants did the shiny, waxed boot affect him. The same object in a social equal left him cold.

A sexual urge in the sense of a homoerotic love was not connected with this situation. The very thought of such a possibility was loathsome to him. But from time to time decidedly lustful images occurred to him of being the servant of his servants, of being allowed as such to take off their boots, preferably to let himself be trodden on by them, or else to be allowed to wax their boots for them. The aristocrat's pride was outraged by such thoughts. The boot ideas were altogether disgusting and embarrassing to him.

His sexual feelings developed early and forcefully. For a while they found expression in lustful thoughts of boots, and from puberty onward in pollutions that accompanied such thoughts.

Apart from this, his spiritual and physical development proceeded uneventfully. The patient was gifted, learned easily, completed his studies, became an officer and a popular personality in society thanks to his distinguished, thoroughly manly appearance and his high position.

He characterized himself as a good tempered, quiet, strongwilled but superficial person. He asserted that he was a passionate hunter and rider and had never had any inclination to female occupations. In the company of ladies he had always felt uneasy; in the ballroom he had been bored. He had never taken interest in a lady of higher class. Among women only plump peasant girls had interested him. However, he had never felt a truly sensual impulse toward such representatives of the female sex. In the theater and the circus he had been interested only in the male figures, but without any sensual feelings toward them. In men only boots excited him, and only if the wearer belonged to the servant class and was handsome. Men of his own class, no matter how beautiful their boots, were wholly indifferent to him.

The patient is still unclear about his sexual orientation, whether he has greater sympathy for one or the other gender.

He believes that originally he had had a greater sense for women, but this sympathy was in any case very weak. He asserts with certainty that the sight of a naked man would be unattractive to him, and that of male genitalia absolutely revolting. In regard to women this was not the case, yet he remained unexcited even in the face of the most beautiful *corpus femininum* [female body]. As a young officer he had now and then had to accompany his comrades to brothels. He was not averse to letting himself be persuaded to do this since he hoped thereby to rid himself of his troubling boot fantasies. He was impotent until he evoked his boot fantasies. Then the act of cohabitation took its normal course, though without a feeling of pleasure. The patient did not feel an urge to intercourse with a woman, each time it required an outer occasion, that is to say, a seduction. Left to himself his *Vita sexualis* [sexual life] consisted of boot reveries and related dreams and pollutions. Since increasingly this was connected to the urge to kiss his servants' boots, to take them off them, and so on, the patient decided to make every effort to rid himself of this horrid urge that was deeply injurious to his sense of self. At that time, at age twenty, he was just in Paris, and he recalled a gorgeous peasant girl back home. He hoped to be able to free himself of his perverse sexual orientation with her help, returned home immediately and sought this girl's favor. It seems that the patient was not by nature of a contrary sexual disposition. He asserts that he then fell really in love with this person, that the sight of her, the touch of her dress made him shudder with desire, and when once she gave him a kiss, he experienced a powerful erection. Only after a year and a half did the patient attain the goal of his wishes with this person.

He was very potent, but ejaculated late, and never had a sense of pleasure from this act.

After about one and a half year's intercourse with this girl, his love for her cooled off as he did not find her as "chaste and pure" as he would have wished. From then on he had to resort to his boot fantasies, which had meanwhile been latent, in order to maintain his potency in intercouse with this girl. In proportion as his potency decreased, the boot fantasies came quite spontaneously. As a result the patient had intercourse with other women. Now and then, when he was attracted to the woman, things went well without the invocation of boot fantasies.

With diminishing potency, that is, sustained only by boot fantasies, his libido toward the other sex declined. It is indicative of the patient's scant libido and weak inclination toward women that even while he was still maintaining sexual relations with the peasant girl, he took to masturbation. He learnt it from Rousseau's *Confessions,* a book he happened to come across. The boot fantasies were immediately fused with the urges in this direction. He had mighty erections, masturbated, experienced on ejaculation a lively sense of pleasure that remained absent at coitus, and at first felt refreshed and stimulated by masturbation.

In time, however, the symptoms of sexual, then of general neurasthenia with spinal irritation appeared. He gave up masturbation for a while, and sought out his previous beloved. But he was now totally indifferent to her, and when he finally failed even with the help of boot fantasies, he withdrew from the woman and reverted to masturbation through which he felt himself protected from the urge to kiss servants' boots, to wax them, and so forth. Nevertheless his sexual position remained embarrassing to him. Occasionally he attempted coitus again and in fact succeeded as soon as he thought of waxed boots. After a lengthier abstinence from masturbation, coitus sometimes succeeded even without that artificial help.

The patient describes himself as sexually very needy. If he has not ejaculated for a long time, he becomes congested, psychologically very upset, tortured by repulsive boot images so that he is forced to coitus or preferably to masturbation.

In the past year he has greatly complicated his moral situation by acceding to his parents' urgent wish that as the last of a rich and noble lineage he should get married. The bride chosen for him is of rare beauty and spiritually very congruent to him. But as a woman she leaves him as cold as every other woman. She satisfies him aesthetically like a favored "work of art." She represents an ideal to him. To honor her platonically would be a form of happiness worth striving for in his eyes, but to possess her as his wife is an embarrassing thought. He knows in advance that he could be potent with her only with the help of boot fantasies. To resort to such means would go against his respect for the lady, his moral and aesthetic feeling for her. If he sullied her with his boot thoughts, she would also lose her aesthetic worth in his eyes, and then he would be totally impotent and she would be revolting to him. The patient regards his position as desperate, and admits that he has recently repeatedly been on the verge of suicide.

He is a highly intelligent man, thoroughly masculine in appearance with pronounced beard growth, a deep voice, normal genitalia. His eyes have a neuropathic expression. No signs of degeneration.

Symptoms of spinal neurasthenia. Efforts to calm the patient and to inspire in him confidence for his future were successful.

The medical advice consisted of medications to combat the neurasthenia, prohibition of masturbation and of further indulgence in boot fantasies. Prospect that with the removal of the neurasthenia cohabitation will be possible without thoughts of boots and that the patient will in time become morally and physically capable of marriage.

Acquired Pathological Contrary Sexual Feelings

Case 51. The metamorphosis of sexual paranoia. N., twenty-three years old, a pianist, was admitted to the Illenau hospital at the end of October 1865. From a family said to be tubercular but not hereditarily tainted (his father and brother died of pulmonary phtisis [tuberculosis]). The patient was a weakly child, scantily gifted except for a one-sided talent for music. He had always been a quirky character, silent, withdrawn, unsociable, rude.

From his fifteenth year onward masturbation. After a few years already neurasthenic complaints (palpitations, fatigue, at times headache, and so forth) appeared together with hypochondriac manifestations. In the past half year his neurasthenia had increased. He now complained of palpitations, headaches, insomnia, became very irritable, seemed sexually very excited, maintained he had to get married as soon as possible for the sake of his health. He fell in love with an artist, but became ill at almost the same time (Sept. 1865) of persecutory paranoia (hostile observations, taunting talk on the streets, poison in his food, a rope across a bridge so that he could not cross it to get to his beloved). Admitted to an insane asylum because of increasing excitement and conflicts with an environment that he perceived as hostile, he presented initially the picture of typical persecutory paranoia along with symptoms of a sexual, then general neurasthenia, but his persecutory delusions did not arise from this neurotic source. Only now and then did the patient hear his environment say: "Now his seed, now his bladder will be removed from him."

In the course of the years 1866–68 the persecutory delusions receded more and more into the background and were largely replaced by erotic ideas. The somatic psychic foundation was a lasting and powerful excitation in the sexual sphere. The patient fell in love with every woman he saw, heard voices urging him to approach her, demanded permission to marry in a commanding tone, and maintained that if he was not granted a wife, he would get consumption. Under continuing masturbation in 1869 already signals of a future feminization appeared. "If he gets a wife, he will love her only platonically." The patient goes on growing more peculiar, lives in an erotic circle of ideas, sees prostitution being carried on everywhere in the institution, occasionally hears voices that impute to him scandalous behavior toward women. He therefore avoids the company of women, and consents to make music among them only if he is provided with two witnesses.

In the course of 1872 the neurasthenia increases significantly. Now the persecutory paranoia also comes to the fore, assuming clinical features through the underlying neurosis. He has olfactory hallucinations, is influenced magnetically, "waves of magnetic damage" assail him (false interpretation of asthenic spinal complaints). Under continuing violent sexual arousal and masturbatory excesses the process of feminization progresses further. The patient is a man only now and then, longs for a wife, and complains bitterly that the shameless prostitution of the men here in the institution makes it impossible for a woman to reach him. He says he is mortally sick as a result of magnetically poisoned air and unsatisfied love. Without love he cannot live; he is poisoned by tingling poison that acts on the sexual urge. The lady he loves is here in the vilest immorality. The prostitutes here in the institution have happiness beds, that is, beds in which one feels ecstasy without making any movement. He has to make do now with a prostitute. He possesses wonderful rays of thought emanating from his eyes that are worth 20 million. Besides these signs of grandiosity there are also persecutory ones—the food is poisoned by venereal excrement, he can taste and smell the poison, he hears infamous accusations and demands an earshutting machine.

From August 1872 onward the signs in the direction of feminization become ever more frequent. He behaves in a fairly affected manner, declares that he can no longer live among drinking and smoking men. He says he thinks and feels like a woman. He wants from now on to be treated as a woman and to be housed in the women's section. He demands sweets and jellies, and fine pastries. When he has tenesmus [urogenital spasms], he asks to be put in an obstetrical section and to be treated like a very sick pregnant woman. The pathological magnetism of male attendants, he says, has an unfavorable effect on him.

Sometimes for a while he still feels himself to be a man, but in a manner indicative of his pathologically altered sexual feelings he begs for satisfaction through masturbation, for marriage without coitus. Marriage, he says, is a system of desire. The girl that he would wish to take for wife would have to be an onanist.

From December 1872 onward his consciousness of his personality changes permanently into a female one.

He says that he had always been a woman, but from his first to his third year a French limb artist had furnished him with male genitalia and had prevented the later emergence of breasts through salves and manipulation of his thorax.

He vehemently demands housing in the women's section, protection from the men wishing to prostitute him, and women's clothing. He might possibly be willing to work in a toy store at sewing and cutout jobs, or to engage in women's work in an accessories store. From the time of his *transformatio sexus* [sexual transformation] the patient begins a new time reckoning. In his memory he perceives his own earlier personality as a cousin.

He speaks of himself in the third person, declares himself to be the Countess V., Empress Eugenie's best friend, demands perfumes, corsets, and so forth. Regards the other men in the section as women, tries to braid his hair, demands oriental creams to remove hair so that there be no doubt as to his female nature. He enjoys singing the praise of onanism for "from the age of fifteen she had been an onanist and had never sought any other sexual satisfaction." Occasionally neurasthenic complaints, olfactory hallucinations and persecutory deliria are still observed. All his experiences up to December 1872 are attributed to the cousin.

The patient can no longer be dissuaded from the delusion of being the Countess V. She asserts that she had been examined by a midwife and found to be a woman. The Countess will not marry because she despises the world of men. As the patient is not given women's clothing and high-heeled shoes, he spends most of the day in bed, behaves like an ailing aristocratic lady, assumes airs and graces, demands confections, etc. His hair is braided as far as possible into a plait, his beard pulled out, and breasts fashioned out of bread.

In 1874 a knee joint shows degeneration that soon turns out to be connected to pulmonary tuberculosis. Death on 2 December 1874. Skull normal. Frontal brain atrophied. Brain anemic. Microcopic examination by Dr. Schule. In the upper layers of the frontal brain the cells are slightly shrunk; numerous fat deposits in the adventitia [innermost connective tissue]; glia [neuroglia system] unchanged, a few pigment particles. The lower layers of the brain normal. Genitalia very large, testicles small, on the whole unchanged.

Inhibitions of Psychic Development

Case 53. A man, forty, married, had for sixteen years exhibited himself and drawn attention to himself through whistling in parks and other public places in front of little girls, women servants, etc. After he had often been beaten by witnesses, he had in future avoided those particular places, had however continued his activities elsewhere. Hydrocephalus. Slight degree of mental weakness. Light sentence.

Acquired Mental Weakness, Probably Due to Lues [Syphilis]

Case 57. Officer X. has repeatedly committed immoral acts with little girls, including having them perform manusturbation on him, showing them his genitalia, and groping theirs.

Formerly healthy and of blameless conduct, X. had got syphilis in 1867. In 1879 paralysis of the left abducent [nerve] set in. Thereafter weakness of memory, changes in his whole temperament and character, headaches, occasional incoherence of speech, reduction of the capacity for clear and logical thought, occasional asymmetry of the pupils, paresis [partial paralysis] of the right facial muscles were noted.

X., thirty-seven years old, showed no trace of lues on examination. The paralysis of the abducent persists. His left eye is amblyopic [poor vision]. He is mentally weakened, asserts in the face of the mass of evidence against him, that it is a matter of a harmless misunderstanding. Traces of aphasia [impaired speech], weakness of memory, especially for recent events, superficiality of emotional reaction, rapid mental exhaustion to the point of loss of memory and of speech. Proof that the ethical defect and the perverse sexual urge are symptoms of a pathological state of the brain probably due to lues.

Suspension of criminal proceedings.

Periodical Insanity

Case 66. Catherine W., sixteen years old, has not yet menstruated. Formerly healthy. Father irascible.

Seven weeks before her admission (3 December 1872) melancholy gloom and irritability. On 27 November attack of frenzy for two days. Then melancholy again. On 6 December normal condition.

On 24 December (twenty-eight days after the first attack of frenzy) quiet, withdrawn, depressed. On 27 December state of exaltation (cheerfulness, laughter, etc.) with fervent love for a female attendant. On 31 December suddenly melancholic catalepsy [rigidity of the limbs] that dissipates after two hours. On 20 January a renewed attack, very similar to the previous one. Again on 18 February together with traces of a period. The patient has total amnesia for what had happened during the paroxysms, and hears with genuine surprise what she is told.

Subsequently still abortive attacks that yield in June with regular periods to complete psychological well-being.

Case 67. A quiet lady, close to menopause. Very bad heredity. In her youth mild attacks of epilepsy. Always eccentric, quick-tempered, strictly moral, childless marriage.

Several years ago, after violent emotional turbulence, an attack of hystero-epilepsy, thereafter post epileptic insanity for several weeks. Then insomnia for several weeks. Subsequently menstrual insomnia and the urge to entice boys under ten, to kiss them and to touch their genitalia. The urge to coitus, altogether to intercourse with any adult is absent at this time.

The patient sometimes speaks openly about her urge, asks us to watch over her as she cannot well control herself. In the intervals she anxiously avoids any discussion of the matter, is very modest, in no way sexually needy.

Hysteria

Case 72. Marianne L. in Bordeaux. At night, while her employers slept deeply under the influence of narcotics she had administered, had delivered their children to her lover for his sexual pleasure and had made them witness immoral scenes. It turned out that L. was hysterical (hemianesthsia and attacks of spasms) and had before her illness been a decent, responsible person. Since her illness she had prostituted herself shamelessly and had lost her moral sense.

Paranoia

Case 73. M. has impregnated his daughter. His wife, the mother of eighteen children and herself pregnant by her husband, lodged a legal complaint. M. had been suffering for two years from religious paranoia. "I had the revelation that I should lie with my daughter, the eternal sun. Then a being of flesh and blood would come into existence through my faith which is 1800 years old. This being would be as a bridge into eternal life between the Old and the New Testament." The madman had carried out this order which was in his opinion divine.

3
Arthur Schnitzler

In his lifetime Arthur Schnitzler was better known as an important figure in Austrian literature than as a medical man, and this still holds true today. From 1885 onward until his death Schnitzler wrote a constant stream of dramas, short stories, and novels; many of them have been translated into other languages, and several have been adapted into films, most recently Stanley Kubrik's *Eyes Wide Shut* (1999) based on *Traumnovelle* (1926; *Dream Novel* [1927], *Dream Story* [1999]). Schnitzler achieved his breakthrough into the literary realm in 1896 with *Liebelei*, which was a great success at Vienna's foremost theater, the Burgtheater; its lasting appeal is attested by repeated translations into English under a variety of titles such as *Light-'o-Love* (1912), *Playing with Love* (1914), *Love Games* (1983), *Dalliance* (1986), *Flirtation* (1999). A complete list of Schnitzler's literary writings is available in *A Companion to the Works of Arthur Schnitzler.*[1]

Before turning primarily to creative writing, Schnitzler had qualified as a physician at the Medical School in Vienna in 1885. In so doing, he was following in the footsteps of his father, Dr. Johann Schnitzler (whose work he mentions in his study of aphonia); Dr. Schnitzler, senior, was a prominent laryngologist who numbered among his patients many of Vienna's leading actors and opera singers so that the young Schnitzler became familiar with the city's glittering artistic life at an early age. He was not an enthusiastic medical student, as he himself confesses in his autobiography, *Jugend in Wien* (pub. 1968; *My Youth in Vienna* [1970]), preferring to patronize theaters, coffeehouses, and horse races. On qualifying as a medical doctor, Schnitzler did his residency at the Allgemeines Krankenhaus, Vienna's vast teaching hospital, and subsequently became a *Sekundararzt* (staff doctor) at the Poliklinik (ambulatory outpatient clinic). He also assumed the editorship of the *Internationale klinische Rundschau* (International clinical review), founded by his father in 1887.

Schnitzler's father evidently hoped that medical journalism would satisfy his son's urge to write. Between 1887 and 1893 Schnitzler contributed some fifty book reviews to the journal (rpt. in Arthur Schnitzler, *Medizinische Schriften*).[2] The range of his interests is remarkably wide; he reviewed books on topics as diverse as the treatment of fevers, experimental pharmacology, the etiology of tuberculosis, therapeutics in internal medicine, syphilis, women doctors, basic concepts in medicine, and the transformation of benign into malignant tumors of the larynx.

But almost half of Schnitzler's reviews in those years were devoted to issues in the borderlands between neurology and psychiatry. Apart from reviewing Charcot's lectures on diseases of the nervous system, S. Weir Mitchell's work on the treatment of neurasthenia, and Krafft-Ebing's volume on sexual deviations, Schnitzler gives particular attention to the question of hypnosis and suggestion. He writes on Auguste Forel's considerations on the uses and significance of hypnotism, Jean Richet's experimental observations on the transfer of thoughts and on so-called clairvoyance, Krafft-Ebing's later experiments with hypnosis, and theories of hypnosis by two Austrian physicians, Schmidkunz and Obersteiner, who have passed into oblivion. Schnitzler expresses his highest admiration for Hippolyte Bernheim, discussing both his landmark study of the practical application of hypnosis and suggestion and its sequel, which addresses specifically the psychotherapeutic potential of this method. Schnitzler bestows utmost praise on Freud's translation of Bernheim's work, citing the lucidity of Freud's prose. From his choice of works to review and his emphases, it becomes apparent that Schnitzler was both fascinated and familiar with hypnotic suggestion as a means to deal with a variety of afflictions prevalent and puzzling in his day.

This, then, is the context for Schnitzler's case study "On Functional Aphonia and Its Treatment by Hypnosis and Suggestion." Schnitzler's only publication in the genre of the case history, it appeared in the *Internationale klinische Rundschau* in 1889. It straddles the fields of laryngology and psychiatry in exploring the possibilities of hypnosis for the physical affliction of loss of voice.

In his assessment of all the cases Schnitzler first proceeds as the internist he had been trained to be rather than as a psychiatrist. He starts each case by taking a thorough medical history of the patient as well as the current health status of his patients' parents and siblings. What he records are predominantly the physical sicknesses such as pneumonia, scrofula, and tuberculosis. While Schnitzler does not directly address heredity, he clearly considers the context of the patient's family medical history an important factor in the total profile as he begins on each case. On only one occasion, with H.W. (case 1), does he mention an immediate psychological trigger to illness when the onset of her epileptic attacks is directly related to the powerful impression of her having seen a man suffer a seizure in the street. Even here, however, the hypothesis that H.W.'s subsequent attacks are imitative in nature stems from the patient herself, not from Schnitzler, who always remains eminently cautious, though not to the point of skepticism. While he uses such standard phraseology as "the patient states/asserts," he does not disbelieve the complaints reported even when he cannot find a physical cause for them. Throughout the hypnotic treatments in all his cases Schnitzler is meticulous in carrying out repeated examinations of the throat and vocal chords to ascertain any changes in the appearance of the affected organs. Schnitzler's reiterated emphasis on his patients' physical condition testifies to the continuing dominance of the somatic approach at the end of the nineteenth century, which had witnessed such momentous progress in the understanding of disease processes. Even while venturing into what would nowadays be called alternative medicine, Schnitzler is punctilious in adhering to the practices of conventional medicine. In contrast to Beard's flamboyant manner and often unsubstantiated claims, Schnitzler comes across as modest, cautious, almost conservative in his experimentation with novel methods.

Schnitzler also conforms to medical conventions in the format of his article. His style fluctuates between, on the one hand, that of clinical notes in which specific details are recorded in sparse, abrupt phrases devoid of verbs or of complete grammatical organization (just as Krafft-Ebing does), and, on the other hand, that of academic prose in long, highly structured, often complex sentences. The scholarly aura is fostered too by the opening series of references to previous cases that form a precedent or a parallel to his own experiences. Schnitzler thus embeds his report in the lineage of current medical research. But, as Janet does a little later, he switches to the present tense to convey vividly the immediacy of his experimentation with the patient. This use of the present tense at crucial points in the hypnotic procedure allows readers to participate vicariously in Schnitzler's tension, his excitement at success, and his disappointment at shortcomings.

Schnitzler lays no claim to being an innovator except in the application of hypnosis and suggestion specifically to aphonia. Yet he constantly applies the word *experimentation* to his treatment of these cases as if fully aware of the research as well as the practical aspects of the work he is recording here. He considers various methods of inducing hypnosis and states that he opts for that of Bernheim, whose work he greatly admired, as is evident from his reviews of Bernheim's books. He mentions the side effects some of his patients experience, notably headaches and a mild sensation of heat together with a reddening of the face, but argues that these are minor, transient inconveniences compared to the healing benefits gained. Schnitzler is quite candid about the fact that some patients are harder to hypnotize than others. The same honesty extends too to his failures. The article is a record of experimentation with mixed outcomes in the considerable variations in the patients' responses. Indeed, it is the unpredictability and waywardness of hypnosis as a mode of treatment that emerge most strongly. Schnitzler neither minimizes the inherent difficulties nor advocates hypnosis as an infallible cure-all. On the contrary, he concedes that he would never dare to put "the bold word 'cured' " at the end of any of his cases because the duration of the success of his treatment is "the dark side of the question," to which no certain answer is as yet possible.

Schnitzler discusses six cases fully and makes passing reference to several others, some his own patients, some drawn from the medical literature. In presenting a series of similar cases he is following the tradition of exploring a number of parallel cases in order to be able ultimately to deduce some general conclusions. However, he admits that six cases are too few to allow definitive findings. The article is therefore essentially modest and rather tentative in tone perhaps because Schnitzler, as an internist, is aware of venturing into a field in which he has more of a strong interest than either training or established expertise. His manner is the diametric opposite to that of his contemporary, Charcot, who projects the assurance that he is in command of all answers.

All six of Schnitzler's cases are women, although in his opening survey of the precedents he adduces two men: one (published by Ariza) a case of aphasia and aphonia following a traumatic head injury that was cured in three hypnotic sessions; the other (reported by Marcel and Marinesco) a "nervous" young man who lost consciousness for thirteen days after a "frightful shock," became aphonic and mute, and eventually had his speech restored by a combination of hypnosis and verbal exercises. Toward the end of his article Schnitzler also mentions having tried to hypnotize "a young lad," but the outcome

was inconclusive because the first attempt had to be broken off and
no further ones were instituted. He therefore has no experience of
the technique with men.

Among the six aphonics, five are young and single, and would normally at that time have been described as "hysterical." Schnitzler is
sufficiently shrewd and enlightened to avoid that blanket designation
(which was, of course, also a judgment and an expression of contempt on the part of male physicians). He states categorically at the
very outset that he prefers the term *functional aphonia* to the more
customary *hysterical aphonia,* and he gives cogent medical reasons for
sidestepping a loaded term. The use of *functional aphonia,* he explains,
is less likely to lead to diagnostic misinterpretations since it may be
caused by other disorders such as tuberculosis or poor nutrition that
create a weakness of the muscles of the larynx. A.R. (case 6), for
example, suffers from tuberculosis, and several of the other patients
too show definite signs of the disease. Schnitzler therefore considers
hysterical inappropriate if there are no other symptoms, specifically
genital ones, apart from the aphonia or if the aphonia might be connected to a physical disorder.

Wisely, Schnitzler treads warily in this area. Hysteria had by the late
nineteenth century become a very widespread, poorly differentiated
diagnosis for many of the ailments that afflicted women. The possibility of hysteria in men was only grudgingly conceded since hysteria
was thought to stem from a displacement of the uterus. However,
Charcot documented the existence of several instances of hysteria in
men (see introduction and Charcot, 129). Nevertheless, when Freud
spoke of male hysteria in his lecture to the Viennese Medical Association in 1886 on his return from five months' study with Charcot in
Paris, he met with taunting derision and incredulity. Hysteria was
regarded as the root of many complaints designated in today's psychiatric nosology as psychosomatic conversion disorders, that is, the manifestation of psychological unease or pain in physical ills that are certainly real subjectively to the patient although devoid of objective
pathological findings. It is this type of perplexing aphonia that Schnitzler chooses to describe as "functional" in contradistinction to organic.
His repeated thorough physical examinations of his patients are motivated by the internist's need to make sure that he is not overlooking a
pathological condition in need of physical treatment rather than a
functional disturbance that could respond to hypnosis and suggestion.

Hypnosis was a dubious form of therapy on the margins of conventional medicine in Schnitzler's day (see introduction). Always

viewed with considerable suspicion, hypnotism was further discredited when it declined into a popular entertainment. The performances of the Danish stage hypnotist Carl Hansen provoked such curiosity (and notoriety) in Vienna in 1880 that the police stopped the demonstrations at the instigation of the medical faculty. Even after its partial rehabilitation for serious medical purposes by Auguste Liébault, Charcot, and Bernheim, hypnosis retained the aura of a rather questionable method.

Schnitzler grasps that its basis is essentially *psychological.* This is in fact by far the most important conclusion he reaches from observing his patients' responses. He notices that hypnosis rarely succeeds at the first attempt but does so much more often subsequently; a precondition for its success is the establishment of a relationship of trust between the "medium," that is, the patient, and the hypnotizer. The necessity for such a rapport is particularly well brought out by the case of A.R. (no. 6), who is very upset—and aphonic—when Schnitzler on one occasion lets another doctor awake her from her hypnotic sleep. He has to start all over again, repeating the hypnosis and the healing suggestion, whereupon her voice returns immediately. However, if she is hypnotized by a colleague of his, the success is transient, lasting at most a few hours. Clearly she is responding not to a mere technique but to a trusted person. Schnitzler comments that the disparity in the effectiveness of hypnosis is "a proof of the medium's habituation to the hypnotizer." It is also significant that H.W. (case 1) does not answer questions put to her by other doctors while under hypnosis by Schnitzler; she is evidently wholly atuned to him. So it is really more than just a matter of habituation; confidence and belief in the known hypnotizer are crucial for the patient's subconscious acceptance of the suggestions. In other words, hypnosis is conceived by Schnitzler not as the physical transaction that Mesmer thought it to be, but as the product of an unspoken contract between the patient and the hypnotizer.

The impact of hypnosis and suggestion thus depends fundamentally on the strength of a positive rapport between the subject and the operator, that is, on the establishment of what would later be called the transference and the therapeutic alliance. In this respect, hypnosis as practiced by Schnitzler foreshadows various later forms of psychotherapy. What is more, Schnitzler's insight into the potential value of hypnosis and suggestion in the medical arena goes beyond the functional aphonia that is his central subject here. In the first case already he proposes the usefulness of this treatment not only in nasal asthma but also in other conditions that are "neurotic reflex reactions" (conversion disorders), not pathological changes in a specific organ. He points out that surgical intervention may be rendered unnecessary by the application of hypnosis. With the nose, he admits, surgical intervention is minimal so that the gain is less great than in the avoidance of surgery to correct disturbances of deep-seated organs such as the female genital system that could instead be remedied by hypnosis with far less trauma.

In the closing paragraphs of his article Schnitzler therefore recommends the extension of hypnosis and suggestion to functional complaints other than aphonia that are likewise fundamentally neurotic in origin. At the very end he pushes the argument in favor of hypnosis even further when he advocates its use even in cases that "*are not really functional in nature*" [sic], for instance to alleviate the pain in an inflamed muscle or to restore its mobility; hypnosis could work in such cases because there is "*a residue of functional involvement*" [sic] in the affected organ so that it can be modified by hypnosis. Although Schnitzler lays no claim to originality and is, on the contrary, concerned to relate his experiments to previous medical research, he is extraordinarily perceptive and prescient in his conceptualization of the potential of hypnosis and suggestion. Yet curiously, perhaps out of caution or because of the association of psychology with philosophy rather than medicine at that time, he does not dwell on the role of psychological factors in both the etiology and the "cure" of functional disturbances. At the end of the case of K.N. (no. 4) Schnitzler remarks, despite his commitment to hypnosis, that marriage and the happiness it brought had done more for her than his treatment without, however, articulating the pscyholgical aspect. Arguably, his comment could be seen as a throwback to the old conception of hysteria as an expression of the unhappiness of the womb, which could be remedied by intercourse and pregnancy. However, Schnitzler never makes the slightest allusion to such an antiquated notion and is altogether too scientifically oriented simply to fall into such a primitive, superstition-laden trap. Similarly, in the case of R.R. (no. 2), he does not seem to realize the implications of the restoration of her health when she leaves the family environment and goes to live with her aunt. In case no. 3 (A.St.), he mentions that "a strong depressive affect again created aphonia" without directly linking cause and effect.

In this respect, especially in his understanding of the importance of the therapeutic alliance, Schnitzler is a forerunner of Freud, although he does not emphasize the connection between the psychological and the physical as explicitly or as forcefully as Freud was to do. Freud and Schnitzler were contemporaries (Freud was six years older than Schnitzler), and they shared a similar personal background. Both came from families of East European Jewish extraction; Freud's father had moved to Vienna from Moravia, while Schnitzler's family had gone to the city from Hungary. Schnitzler was the more privileged of the two: not only was he already born in Vienna, a distinct advantage in that prejudice-ridden milieu, but also the Schnitzlers were prosperous so that they were able by the early 1880s to relocate from Leopoldstadt, the traditional Jewish immigrant quarter, to the more elegant inner city. Freud, whose father was a modest grain merchant, could himself replicate this move only later. Both attended the Medical School in Vienna at about the same time, Freud from 1873 to 1881, Schnitzler from 1879 to 1885, so that they were taught by some of the same teachers, notably the psychiatrist Theodor Meynert. Both likewise cut loose from their Jewish roots without going as far as a formal apostasy. Both also relinquished conventional career paths in medicine, Freud by developing psychoanalysis, and Schnitzler through his pursuit of literary activity.

However, despite their common background and the fact that they lived in fairly close proximity in the same city, they had little personal contact, meeting only very rarely. Indeed, a certain tension undeniably existed between them. Schnitzler is known to have harbored reservations about some of Freud's psychoanalytic tenets, particularly incest and infantile sexuality, and Freud for his part soon abandoned the practice of hypnosis, in which Schnitzler believed, in favor of the free association that is the method of psychoanalysis. Nevertheless, Freud and Schnitzler have often been termed "Doppelgänger" (doubles), a view that proves on examination to be too simplistic. It originates in a letter of May 14, 1922, sent by Freud to Schnitzler on the occasion of his sixtieth birthday. Freud does in fact use the word *Doppelgänger*, but he appends to it *Scheu* (reluctance), describing his relationship to Schnitzler as one of "Doppelgängerscheu."[3] The added little word *Scheu* introduces a totally new dimension by undercutting the doubling with a strain of avoidance. Freud believed that Schnitzler had acquired his insights through intuition, whereas he himself was very insistent on the scientific nature of his own observations that formed the basis of psychoanalysis. This contrast between what Freud regarded as Schnitzler's imaginative manner and his own scientific approach was, in a rather complex way, to be the crux of the problematic relationship between this pair of alleged "doubles."[4]

One important way in which this difference surfaced is in the mode in which Schnitzler and Freud wrote their case histories, and beyond that in their respective attitudes toward their writing, although not in the manner that might be expected of Schnitzler's bias to the imaginative and Freud's to the scientific. To the contrary, there is a distinct chiasmus in their choice of styles for their case histories. In consonance with the conventions of nineteenth-century medical discourse, Schnitzler presents his cases in a terse, abbreviated manner, stripped of any personal detail other than what is medically relevant. Freud, on the other hand, composed lengthy, expansive biographies of his patients that take full account of their social context and relationships. He did so because he sought to expose the often largely concealed conflicts and dissonances intrinsic to his patients' position in their environment that he identified as a major source of their neuroses. Yet he was concerned by the resultant wealth of circumstantial detail and the apparent discursiveness of his case histories, in short, their closer affinity with the novelistic than with the scientific. He himself expressed his anxiety on this count in the *Studies on Hysteria* (1896), "dass die Krankengeschichten, die ich schreibe, wie Novellen zu lesen sind" ("that my case histories read like novels").[5] He feared that they would thereby forfeit the imprint of serious scientific scholarship and even assured his readers that he had been properly trained as a neurologist in local diagnosis, the application of electrotherapy, and similar normative medical treatments of his day. Yet, ironically, it is as an outstanding German stylist (he was awarded the Goethe Prize in 1930) and as a humanist that Freud is read nowadays. But in his own time, especially at the beginning of his career as a psychoanalyst, he worried about bucking the conventions.[6]

While Freud thus conflates his medical and his literary aptitudes, Schnitzler, on the contrary, segregates them. His writing on functional aphonia, though by no means devoid of imagination, gives no overt indication of his capacity as a creative writer. Only later, after his father's death, did Schnitzler turn away from the practice of medicine in favor of devoting himself fully to artistic pursuits. His signal success with *Liebelei* in 1896 was followed by a prodigious, high-quality literary output in drama and narrative right up to his death in 1931. The two facets of his life did remain linked insofar as many of his works portray characters who are either psychopathic or have recognizably abnormal traits. The titular persona in *Frau Beate und ihr Sohn* (1913; Beate and her son) instigates her drowning and her son's out of a sense of guilt at her own rash conduct and the fear of the damage it might inflict on her son. *Doktor Gräsler Badearzt* (1917; Doctor Gräsler: Spa physician) opens with the mysterious suicide of the doctor's sister, and he himself is prey to a chronic inability to make vital decisions that ruins his prospects for happiness. The narrator of the interior monologue *Fräulein Else* (1924; Miss Else) ends by committing suicide. In the novel *Therese: Chronik eines Frauenlebens* (1928; Theresa: Chronicle of a woman's life) Theresa's illegitimate son robs and murders her. The central character, Robert, in Schnitzler's last work, *Flucht in die Finsternis* (1931; Flight into darkness), suffers from progressive delusional paranoia that leads him to kill his doctor brother before himself vanishing in the mountains. While openly embracing the profession of writer, Schnitzler subsumed into it his medical knowledge, whereas Freud insisted on his scientific aims, to which his literary abilities were, so to speak, incidental.

But beneath this disparity between Schnitzler and Freud there is another kind of parallelism. Each, albeit in a different way, was instrumental in the migration of the psychiatric case history into the domain of literature around the turn of the century. Again, the paths they chose diverged. Freud effected this metamorphosis by writing case histories that read, as he himself lamented, like stories such as *Bruchstück einer Hysterie-Analyse* (1905; *Fragment of an Analysis of a Case of Hysteria*, known familiarly as *Dora*), *Rattenmann* (1909; *Ratman*), and *Wolfsmann* (1918; *Wolfman*), to name just the preeminent ones. These case histories have the artistic disposition, the suspense, the capacity to engage readers that are the hallmarks of literary works. Schnitzler's case histories of functional aphonia are by comparison relatively flat and dominated by technicalities; the figures remain less vivid to readers because they are sketched only in barest outline as representative of a dysfunctional state. The richness of detail and the human complexity that draw readers so powerfully into the predicaments and neuroses of Freud's patients recur in Schnitzler's fictional writings as he explores imaginatively his invented characters' psychopathic traits.

To this extent, then, Freud and Schnitzler are indeed "Doppelgänger," although in the sense of reverse mirror images of each other. Literary works, notably those of the school known as naturalism, had earlier already to some extent appropriated materials from the psychiatric case history, for instance in Ibsen's dramas and Zola's novels. However, Ibsen and Zola were amateurs in psychopathology. Schnitzler and Freud, through their professional training, endowed their narratives with the authenticity of genuine expertise. But Schnitzler kept the genre of the case history separate from that of his fictions, while in Freud the two became inextricably fused.

On Functional Aphonia and Its Treatment by Hypnosis and Suggestion

Internationale klinische Rundschau 3 (1889)

In the following pages several cases of functional aphonia will be reported; in light of the treatment method applied to them, especially the current debate about hypnosis, they should not be entirely without interest.

I chose the phrase *"functional aphonia"* instead of the more customary *"hysterical aphonia"* because it is more likely to exclude diagnostic misinterpretations. If a patient presents other symptoms from the rich spectrum of hysterical phenomena besides aphonia, for which no anatomical cause can be found, then the diagnosis of hysterical aphonia will indisputably stand; irrespective of whether we concur with those who want to regard all hysteria as a real psychosis or we agree with those who speak of hysteria only if the connection with a disturbance of the genital system can be proven. There can also be no doubt that some of those forms of aphonia that are readily and simply designated as hysterical seem to be amenable to explanation in other ways. General nutritional disorders, especially tuberculosis and chlorosis, certain neuroses such as neurasthenia, seem to create a functional weakness in the muscles of the larynx, as in other groups of muscles, that often demand an increase in nerve energy. Indeed, in such cases we will perhaps sometimes elicit not only a normal functioning of the nerves through our therapeutic intervention but even a heightening of the normal nerve energy that will allow the fatigued muscles to carry out the necessary work, just as an energetic general has to be put at the head of a weakened army.

In such cases, however, we will apply the same therapeutic methods as in the truly hysterical disturbances but then we may not speak of hysterical aphonia despite the lack of evident anatomical causation, despite the not uncommon spontaneous disappearance of the symptom, despite the effect of some antihysterical medications—this fact becomes clear from the genesis of the disturbance. At any rate, a plethora of purely hysterical aphonias will remain.

The following cases, which could certainly be much expanded, are to be considered especially in regard to the therapeutic method of suggestion that was applied to them; they do not pretend to present anything fundamentally new; rather they want to show in only a few examples the influence of hypnosis and suggestion, this healing method that is still in need of further clarification. The publications on the influence of this method on the type of illnesses under discussion are not yet numerous enough, in our country, to make new evidence seem entirely worthless.

It is in the nature of the issue if, in the course of the hypnosis, I touch on procedures not directly connected to aphonia, and for this reason an occasional digression will have to be excused. Besides, there will be opportunity to report on successes in healing that I had the good fortune to attain in other neuroses and in some of these cases to go into the distinctive phenomena of somnambulism.

The method that I used to induce hypnosis in the majority of cases makes the patients look steadily into my eyes or to stroke their forehead, temple, or eyelids with my hand. The well known fact that the induction of hypnosis in a person becomes easier the more often it is applied hardly needs to be mentioned, and in all the medical—apologies for this now trite phrase because of its brevity and validity—that I frequently hypnotized, ten to thirty seconds of stroking the eyelids or quietly spoken persuasion, not always in an "imperious tone" were mostly enough to induce hypnosis. It is therefore the method of *Bernheim*'s school that I apply.

I cannot yet address the debate about the harmful influence of hypnosis, that has lately been so heated, because the number of my observations is too small and the time span in which I gathered my experiences too limited. As far as I can tell from the literature, those who express the most negative opinions on the consequences of hypnosis are those who have the least experience of it. Any final judgment is as of now premature. Yet a very scholarly German Medical Society rejected the procedure outright when it was demonstrated. However, premature prejudice is better than premature enthusiasm; the latter leads to disappointments, the former to surprises that are preferable.

The idea of curing functional aphonia by suggestion certainly predates the medical application of hypnotism in recent years. I cannot suppress the comment that in our day the attempt to find analogies for suggestion in our ordinary lives seems to go too far: pedagogy is suggestion; great men were really suggestors. The founders of religions used suggestion, and whole tribes were their media. The involuntary tyranny that significant minds exercise over smaller ones is suggestion, and if we resolve to get up at five in the morning and do not oversleep, we have performed an autosuggestion. Now I have to concede that it is one thing if I suggest to someone that he should bring me an apple from a tree and he carries out my demand, and another if I induce hypnosis in a healthy person, who has never heard of hypnosis, tell him he will wake with paralysis of the left arm and then actually see that on waking this person cannot move his left arm without any idea of what I told him in his sleep. These are obviously very heterogeneous things that I contrast with each other here, and there are undoubtedly intermediary stages that daily life, world history, and finally pathology provide for us; nonetheless the word suggestion has recently become somewhat cheapened, and the theory of the transfer of one's own will to another person is by no means as much a matter of course as some people like to portray it. The cases of functional aphonia in which it suffices to say, Try it, you can speak, do not strictly speaking belong in a treatise on the influence of hypnotic suggestion on aphonia. Still, these suggestions will have to be taken into special consideration in the discussion of the relevant questions in the waking state, although later experiences will show that the suggestions in the waking state and those in hypnotic sleep were not as closely related as standard teachings used to make us believe.

It is well known that more or less energetic persuasion can sometimes have good results; it is also known that a sudden fright or some other emotional shock can make aphonia, like other functional disturbances, disappear, and sometimes such patients regain their voices just as suddenly as they had lost them (autosuggestion maybe?). Electrical currents have also sometimes helped, mainly because the patient believed in their efficacy, which does not reduce their truly extraordinary effectiveness in functional aphonia.

Cures of aphonia through genuine suggestion have been published primarily by *Bernheim*. In his brilliant work *De la suggestion et de ses applications à la thérapeutique* [On suggestion and its applications in therapeutics] there are several cases that have a bearing here.

Observation no. 27 tells of a thirty-year-old woman who exhibited a variety of hysterical symptoms as well as aphonia for two years. After several failed attempts, the patient's voice was successfully restored through hypnotic suggestion. Two years later, further loss of voice, which has not yet been restored after fourteen days' application of electricity.

Observation no. 28 deals with a 55-year-old nervous woman who was hoarse every winter for six weeks. Cured by one-time hypnotic suggestion.

Observation no. 30 tells how a tubercular girl was cured of her aphonia by simple assertion ["*par simple affirmation*"], after the induction apparatus had been brought. Afterward the patient was hypnotized for other reasons.

In observation 60 aphonia appeared in a fifteen-year-old girl after an attack of pneumonia. Three hypnotic sessions revealed that the patient was easy to hypnotize; but they remained therapeutically unproductive, as did the fourth one. After hypnosis *Bernheim* tried suggestion in a waking state, initially encountered disbelief, but was able by energetic affirmation ["*par affirmation énergique*"] finally to bring her to speak fairly loudly so that the patient was in full possession of her voice the next day. As far as I can tell from the account of the illness, no laryngoscopic examination was ever carried out.

Bottey presented a case of hysterical aphonia to the *Soc. méd. prat. de Paris* [Society for Practical Medicine] on 28 September 1887; the illness, that had subsisted for eighteen months with unsuccessful treatment by hydrotherapeutic and electrical measures, was cured in five hypnotic sessions.

Ariza in *Corr. Méd. Castellaneo Salamanca* [Medical Reports of Salamanca] of 10 July 1888, published a case of traumatic aphasia and aphonia (head injury); the aphonia disappeared after the second hypnotic session; after the third hypnotic session the patient pronounced the suggested words correctly, but still had difficulty with other words; in the end he was able to speak well.

Boland (*Verviers*) in *Extrait des annales de la société méd. chir. de Liège* [Excerpt from the Annals of the Medical and Surgical Society of Liège] of 1887 cured six cases of hysterical aphonia by suggesting to the patients that they would be able to speak after the insertion of the laryngoscope.

Joh. Schnitzler in the *Inter. klin. Rundschau* [International Clinical Revew] August 1888 reports a case of paralytic aphonia and spastic dyspnea [shortness of breath] in a twenty-year-old girl, cured by hypnosis, and mentions having cured other similar cases in like manner.

A very interesting treatise on hysterical speechlessness was published by Dr. *Natier* in the *Revue mensuelle de laryngologie, d'otologie et de rhinologie* [Monthly Journal of Laryngology, Otology, and Rhinology], edited by Dr. *Moure*. It came out under the title "Contribution to the Study of Hysterical Mutism" in numbers 4, 5, 8, and 9 of the 1888 issue. This article's theme does not overlap with the topic under discussion here; however, there are numerous points of contact. The combination of hysterical mutism and hysterical aphonia is not too rare; I shall have occasion to report a related case. *Natier* too writes about several such cases, and I mention especially those that are suited to demonstrating the influence of hypnotic suggestion.

Thus *Natier* cites an observation of *Amadei* in the *Gazzetta degli Ospitali* [Hospitals' Gazette] no. 12, 1887, in which a forty-three-year-old woman, who was suffering from various hysterical symptoms, became more aphonic and finally mute. Hypnotism effected a cure after several sessions in which the patient—beginning with the pronunciation of letters and syllables—was gradually brought to speak.

A similar success was achieved in another case taken from the *Archives roumaines de médic. et chirurg.* [Roumanian Archives of Medicine and Surgery], 1887, *E. Marcel* and *G. Marinesco.*

A nervous young man of nineteen loses consciousness for thirteen days after a frightful shock. He suffers from hysteroepileptic attacks, is aphonic and mute; indeed he can barely write. Later, at night in dreams a few confused words come from his mouth. The patient slowly regains the ability to write, but not to speak. The usual treatments are applied in vain, including hypnotism and suggestion. It is only the combination of hypnotism with vocal exercises ["*en associant à l'hypnotisme la gymnastique vocale*"] that restores speech to him.

Natier also cites a twenty-year-old woman observed by *Dello Strogolo* (Morgagni, 1887), who exhibited various hysterical symptoms, mutism and aphonia after a severe fright. In hypnotic sleep the restoration of her voice was suggested to her, and on wakening she said in a loud voice: I am cured.

The case by *Urechia* in *Annales médico–psych.* [Annals of Psychological Medicine] no. 3, 1888 is also cited too by *Natier.* A thirty-two-year-old hysterical woman is struck totally dumb by a violent emotion. In hypnotic sleep she at first resists suggestions, but finally gives in when they are emitted in a more commanding tone.

Boland, too, reports a case of nervous aphonia *(Scalpel,* June 1888) that was cured by suggestion in the waking state.

Finally I still want to mention a quotation from *Bernheim* (loc. cit., p. 278) taken from *Hack Tuke.* Dr. *John Tanner* is said to have cured more than fifty cases of hysterical aphonia through the simple application of an electromagnet to the tongue. It was, however, necessary to convince the patient beforehand that he would indeed be cured by this method.

Before I proceed to consider my cases, I want to make it clear that I never hypnotized except in the presence of other doctors (heads of departments, assistants, students at the Policlinic). This has to be emphasized because the general mistrust of the subject under discussion here has not yet been dissipated. Not without some justification, the thought of deceived observers comes to mind more than that of new truths. But like blind faith, there is blind doubt, both of which greatly inhibit the march of progress.

I now begin to report on my cases.

1. H.W., seventeen years old, states that her parents are alive, her father is healthy, her mother suffers from epilepsy, only since the age of fifty (?); three of her siblings have died, a brother (at age six) of smallpox, another (at age eight) of a lung disease, a sister (four years old) of inflammation of the brain, two brothers are alive, one of them suffering from a discharge from the ear that makes him hard of hearing, the other very easily becomes hoarse, otherwise he is healthy. A brother of her father's is said to suffer from epilepsy which began after a fall. The patient herself had had measles as a small child; eight years ago she was operated on a scrofulous gland on her neck. Every year since the second year of her life she has had open ulcers on her scalp for one to two months in June and July that heal through application of external medications and the ingestion of cod-liver oil. Two years ago in spring she got ulcers on a finger that required surgery.

Eight years ago the patient suffered epileptic attacks. Two weeks before the first attack the patient had seen a man fall down on the street with epileptic seizures; this made such an extraordinarily powerful impression on her that she is inclined to see it as the opportunistic cause of her own illness, which manifested itself at the outset with great violence. At the beginning she had ten to twelve attacks a day; she often bit her tongue during these attacks, and for some time—up to several hours—afterward she was "lost in the head." She was initially treated by Prof. *Benedikt,* later also by another doctor whose name she cannot recall; she took bromides which reduced the incidence of the attacks. They occurred only once a day, later weekly, then monthly; the patient had the last attack three years ago. The patient has been menstruating since her sixteenth year. For the past two years the patient always became hoarse mornings and evenings; for the last two months she has been totally aphonic by day too.

We are dealing with an anemic and sickly girl. The patient's intelligence is commensurate with her age. On the left side of her neck a scrofulous scar. At the base of the right lung the breathing is somewhat weakend; otherwise no physical changes are evident. The heart tones of the patient, who has for years been suffering from mild palpitations, are clear. In her larynx signs of a mild chronic catarrh. In addition, pronounced paresis of the adductor muscles is present; the vocal cords move only slightly at phonation, a broad triangular space remains between them. The patient has already been treated for months with anticatarrhal remedies.

On 29 November I hypnotized her for the first time, which was easily done. I suggest to her: when you wake, you will have a beautiful, clear voice. By calling her I woke her a few minutes later. She woke with a completely clear voice—to her own greatest astonishment. She felt no lassitude nor did she complain of anything else.

On the next day, 30 November, she was again aphonic. She had retained her voice until 4 p.m., at any rate a longer time than in the previous months. I hypnotized her again. After waking she complained of a sensation of heat in her face and indeed during her hypnotic sleep her normally pale face reddened visibly and vividly.

On 1 December she could already report to me that her voice had remained totally good until 8 p.m., and today too the patient was not wholly aphonic, only a little hoarse. No hypnosis.

On 3 December she reported that since the previous day in the morning she was again wholly voiceless. The appearance of her larynx had also changed. It no longer showed a typical paresis of the adductor muscles; the vocal cords gaped at phonation in the cartilaginous part while they closed in the membranous part. In fact I as well as other observers of the laryngoscopic picture could not rule out the view that in the area of the adductor muscles only a spasm was taking place since the vocal cords attained a complete closure in the membranous part. This change in the picture is in fact a frequent occurrence in functional aphonia. Hypnosis and suggestion were again applied. She woke with a completely clear voice, and had maintained it on her return two days later (5 December). Examination with the laryngoscope showed that phonation was no longer as clear as before and a relatively wide gap remained between the vocal cords. Indeed, the gap was so wide that during the laryngoscopic examination total aphonia might have been expected. But this too is a frequent feature precisely in functional aphonia, namely, that the intensity of the sound does not wholly coincide with the movements of the laryngeal muscles that we could see. Evidently the participation of the expelled stream of air in the formation of sounds is quite unstable in just these patients. That is the only way to explain why we observe a worse voice despite better closing vocal cords one day, and on another a better voice despite a widely yawning gap. The patient came back on 7 December in excellent shape.

On 15 January she appeared again and reported that her condition as well as her voice had been very good until two days previously. At any rate some success already considering that the patient had for two months been unremittingly aphonic and for two years aphonic mornings and evenings. Yesterday (14 January) she became hoarse. Today she is totally aphonic. In the course of the day before she had also had attacks of suffocation (spasms). Picture of the larynx: paresis of the adductor muscles.

Hypnosis. Suggestion. Waking with voice.

On 29 January she came again. One afternoon ten days previously she had an attack of a vehement cramp-like pain in the larynx (not a typical attack of suffocation), after which she became voiceless for several hours, and according to her account felt an unpleasant smell coming from her mouth. Today she has regained her voice.

Hypnosis. The reflexes of her patillary sinews appear to be heightened during hypnotic sleep. The sensitivity of her skin is extinct without any suggestion concerning it. I make her get up. She remains standing. Her arms remain in the position indicated by me. I now ask her: Where are you? In a room. Whose room? She gives my name. Only then do I suggest to her the disappearance of the complaints she presented today, and that she remember nothing of what had happened during the sleep. This was clearly a mistake. I had by suggestion removed the healing suggestion. Although this error, as can be seen in other cases, does not always rebound in a lack of success in healing, yet, it seems to me, one has to take care to make the healing suggestion only after amnesia in regard to the other experiments has been suggested. However, as is known, amnesia generally occurs after frequent hypnotic sessions without having to be elicited by suggestion, and the sick person saves only the healing suggestion as a posthypnotic suggestion from the artificial sleep into her natural life even if she is not receptive to other posthypnotic suggestions.

I now wake her by gently blowing on her. She had "slept tight," has no idea that she had spoken to me. According to her perception, she had slept for two hours; actually it had been a mere five minutes.

The next day (30 January) she came with the complaint that in the afternoon she had again felt that cramp-like pain in her larynx. She had her voice. I hypnotize her. At my request she stands up, moves forward and backward. I ask: Where are you? She: At the policlinic. To whom are you speaking? She answers with my name. Others among the doctors present ask: "Who am I?" She always answers by naming me. A not uninteresting variant on that very common phenomenon whereby the hypnotized do not register others' questions and commands and therefore do not react. Moreover, the suggestion that she was now in a different place or that she was a different person did not succeed with W. although it can be achieved with other people hypnotized to this degree. Again a vivid redness of the face developed; she says spontaneously: I am very hot. The suggestion of a cold shower remained wholly without effect. It is apparent that in this patient no high degree of suggestibility had been attained, that to a certain degree the logic of facts was stronger than the hypnotizer's will. This time (after a successful healing suggestion) I had suggested to her that on waking she would remember everything and gradually—a few minutes after waking—she could tell me everything including my failed suggestions.

The next day, 31 January, she came with some hoarseness, but she reported that neither pain nor an attack of suffocation had occurred.

Having induced hypnosis I say to her: Go on sleeping but open your eyes. At first her efforts were in vain; only when I said: "It's quite easy," did she open her eyes. Both eyes are turned inward and downward, converging to a quite extreme degree. I ask her: Can you see anything? She: No.—I: What time is it? She: Ten o'clock at night.—I: Why? She: Because it is very dark. The suggestion of daylight fails.

However, suggestions that after waking she request a hat from one gentleman and a pair of glasses from another are successful; but she declares that she had to do it because I had told her to. Her voice, which had already no longer shown any trace of hoarseness during the hypnosis, is completely clear and beautiful after she wakes. Today after the hypnosis she feels much better than before.

Because of her accounts of attacks of suffocation, her nasal cavities were again inspected more closely, revealing hypertrophic rhinitis, especially on the left side. It is well known how frequently such conditions are found without reflex symptoms, and undoubtedly the ultimate causes for the development of spastic aphonia, of glottal spasms, and attacks of asthma are to be sought not in the nasal illness but in some intermediary factor in the sick person's individuality. It now seems as if it might be possible to overcome this heightened reflex irritability through hypnosis, that properly applied hypnosis, for instance in the case of nasal asthma, could achieve the same treatment of the nose itself. In cases where the necessary surgical intervention is minimal, not much is gained by this method. But in other neurotic reflex reactions, where the relevant organ is harder to access and where the intervention would have to be more radical, it is certainly preferable to treat the heightened reflex irritability than the organ blamed for the disorder; think, for example, of the surgeries that sometimes have to be performed on the female genital system because of reflex neuroses!

Nonetheless in the current case I had the left side cauterized by galvanization on 6 February; I did this after I had hypnotized the patient, and I let her hold the nasal mirror herself during the little intervention in her cataleptic state. On awaking she complained of slight pain in the cauterized area; this would hardly have happened if I had beforehand suggested to her an absence of pain on waking. I believe I must assume this on the analogy of a case I saw Professor *Weinlechner* operate on in his department (Dr. *Jul. Fürth* published the case at the time): the hypnotized subject felt no trace of pain after the operation (the excision of scar tissue on one side of the face) as a result of suggestion.

The conclusions that can be drawn from the case I have just reported are self-evident. An anemic young woman with a history of scrofula and epilepsy suffers for years from aphonia: for two years she is aphonic mornings and evenings, for two months totally. The first hypnotic sessions restore her voice for several hours, the following ones for days and weeks. Laryngospastic attacks, which occur meanwhile, are likewise made to disappear through hypnosis. Today she feels well, and if the aphonia or a laryngospasm should recur, which is not impossible, she can no doubt be freed of it for a long period within a few minutes. It is hardly acceptable to hold the mild sensation of heat, which mostly appeared toward the end of hypnotic sleep, as a serious damaging effect of the hypnosis when set against the advantages enumerated in this case. Another of my patients, who suffered from nervous breathing difficulties (and who, let me add in parentheses, felt better after two hypnotic sessions than in the previous three years), always had a pronounced feeling of cold during hypnotic sleep and for a few minutes afterward. It was, however, possible to remove this unpleasant side effect through suggestion, a strategy that did not succeed with W.

2. R.R., twenty-seven years old, single, servant, has menstruated regularly since the age of sixteen. Parents alive and healthy. A brother died in his twenty-sixth year of "bloody vomiting" following lung disease. Three other siblings are alive and well. The patient, who is not intelligent and very run-down, has been sickly since her youth. From her tenth to her fourteenth year she had suffered from "head pains." When she moved to an aunt, her health was restored. But soon the patient began to cough and to suffer from chest pains. Seven years ago already she was in treatment at the Policlinic; at that time the tonsillectomy was performed; and on the same day she suddenly lost her voice. After some time she regained her voice, only to lose it again more recently, a change that was repeated with extraordinary frequency. For three years she was always hoarse or voiceless; she has now been in possession of her voice for three months, but lately it sounds rough. I observed the patient only on 16 December when she had suddenly lost her voice again. I was told that she had suffered from blennorrhea [discharge] from the larynx and the trachea. Today the patient complains of a feeling of heaviness in her chest, especially in the area of the sternum. She suffers from insomnia as she is plagued particularly at night by violent coughing that sometimes produces a profuse pus-laden discharge. Sometimes, the patient says, the sputum is tinged with blood.

In the past three weeks night sweats, shivering in the evening. Headaches toward nightfall. Hitherto the treatment of the laryngitis consisted of painting her throat with a 10–20 percent iodine solution, the application of electricity to the larynx without, however, any impact on the restoration of the voice.

Examination of the lungs revealed a mild shortness of breath as well as a diffuse bronchial catarrh; the larynx in a chronic catarrhal state; the false voice cords significantly swollen, the real ones thickened and grayish in color. No signs of syphilis. At phonation the vocal cords close in their membranous parts; and the swollen false cords become superimposed on them; in the cartilaginous part a triangular gap.

On 19 December, given the patient's total aphonia, hypnosis was tried for the first time. It never succeeds completely. The patient can be brought to the point where she cannot open her eyes. When her eyes are closed by suggestion, she can through repeated orders be brought to speak. If this suggestion is attempted without beforehand having got her to shut her eyes, it invariably fails. So far it has not been possible to achieve deeper levels of hypnosis. Success with this patient never lasted more than a few days; the extensive disturbances in the sick organs must be taken into consideration. In the past few days laryngeal faradization succeeded in restoring her voice for a few hours. The patient's voice is always rough, a roughness caused by the swelling of the tissues in the voicebox. The conditions of the patient's life are extremely unfavorable, and I doubt any further success.

What is interesting in this case from our point of view is that from day to day the voice could be restored with certainty by *one* means after all others had been proved unreliable, that suggestion of a loud voice was effective only when her eyes were firmly closed by suggestion.

After suggestion the picture of the larynx at phonation shows simple, mild paresis of the adductor muscles.

3. A.St., a locksmith's daughter, sixteen years old, single. Her mother had died of tuberculosis; her father is alive and healthy. Two sisters stillborn. A brother died at ten months of "pains." Ten living siblings.

The patient had diphtheria at age six, allegedly in July 1888.—Has been menstruating since the age of eleven, generally with cramps. From December 1887 to the end of February 1888 she was hospitalized in Prof. v. *Schrötter*'s department with typhus; from March until May she says she spat blood; she remembers once having vomited blood. On 25 July she had herself admitted to the above named department because of abdominal pain; on the day after admission, according to her account, she suddenly lost her voice; she was treated with inhalations and electricity. She was also hypnotized several times. The notes kindly put at my disposal from Prof. v. *Schrötter*'s clinic contain the comment that she was suffering from a mild, chronic catarrh of the larynx. At intonation cramp of the adductor muscles followed by spasm of the abductor muscles. From more recent reports I gather that she was hypnotized a number of times, but that success ensued only after the first time insofar as the patient was not totally aphonic on the day after hypnosis, but could speak in a fairly hoarse voice. Further attempts at healing suggestion remained completely without success; waking her out of the hypnotic sleep was very difficult.

On 16 October she came to the policlinic complaining of voicelessness since 26 July.

The patient is well developed for her age. Her facial color is healthy. The exhalation on the left tip of the lung is somewhat labored. Spleen enlarged. Pain on pressure to the left abdominal area; no pain in the ovaries. No loss of sensitivity in the skin or the mucous membranes. The larynx in a state of chronic catarrh, the vocal cords discolored grayish, the false vocal cords slightly swollen and reddish. Examination shows that on attempting to phonate the vocal cords come nearer up to a certain point, then quickly move apart.

16 October. Hypnosis. Suggestion that she will wake having regained her voice. Deep sleep in which she absolutely does not react to being addressed. She awakes with a violent headache and a very reddened face, but aphonic as before. The headache lasts until evening.

19 October. Hypnosis. Neither she nor I was particularly confident of this attempt. Suggestion that she would wake in full possession of her voice. She wakes with a reddened face and a headache; has *regained her voice.*

20 October. The patient had a mild headache yesterday. Mild hoarseness. No abnormal movement of the vocal cords.

23 October. Was able to speak until the evening of 20 October. While with her family and their friends in a musty inn she suddenly lost her voice when she wanted to say goodnight. The laryngoscope shows abnormal movement of the vocal cords, the patient is totally aphonic.—Hypnosis. Loss of consciousness. It is difficult to wake the patient. Neither calling out to her nor shaking her has any effect. By slightly stroking her on the nose I wake her. She groans and has a headache. Her voice had returned completely. On the next day she was a little hoarse, two days thereafter in complete possession of her voice. In the middle of December she came several times to the outpatient clinic with the complaint that she felt a burning in her throat. No sign of paresis in the adductor muscles; mild catarrh that was treated in the appropriate manner. She does not return until 4 February—totally aphonic. She reports that she had suddenly lost her voice three days before. Pronounced deep redness of the mucous membranes of the pharynx and the larynx; at the attempt to phonate a yawning gap in the cartaliginous area of the vocal cords. She complains of vehement pain and maintains that this time hypnosis will be useless. As I question her more closely, she explains that three days before she had by mistake drunk a very diluted lye solution; since then she has the most terrible difficulties in swallowing and pain in her throat; her voice too had disappeared immediately. Close inspection of her mouth and throat reveal hardly anything new beyond the already noted redness. Erosion of the tongue, no corrosion. The aphonia has naturally to be perceived as functional. The patient is sent away with the necessary instructions and told to return on the next day. She does indeed come the next day with a totally normal voice;

on insertion of the laryngoscope she immediately loses her voice, and the laryngoscopic picture shows paresis of the adductor muscles. When the laryngoscope is removed, the voice is normal again.

She returns on 8 March. She has been aphonic for five days. She is being examined in Prof. *Albert's* clinic for an esophageal stricture resulting from the poisoning by the lye. Laryngoscopic picture: paresis with occasional indication of abnormalities in the movement of the vocal cords.—Hypnosis. She wakes with a headache and voiceless —both suggestions had failed. On the next day she tells me that in fact she "always" suffers from headaches and is generally hoarse before breakfast. Hypnosis. This time the suggestion is successful, and she wakes with a completely clear voice. Curiously, five months previously, when I undertook the first attempt with hypnosis with her, only the second hypnotic session was effective.

To sum up the case: we are dealing with functional aphonia in a young girl weakened by a serious illness of three months' duration she had previously had. The first hypnotic session was unsuccessful, the second restored her voice for three days, the third for more than three months, after which a strong depressive affect again created aphonia for a period of three times twenty-four hours. A further relapse is cured in two hypnotic sessions. Renewed relapses cannot be ruled out, but the therapy is at hand. The headaches following the various hypnotic sessions could unfortunately not be avoided by suggestions about them; however, this drawback is insignificant as against the great advantages of the hypnosis. We have to consider whether we are not encountering an effect other than that of the hypnotic suggestion. Since every other suggestion fails except that aimed at the return of the voice, it is legitimate to ask whether it is not *the psychic effect of the hypnosis as such* that represents its operative momentum. It is surely advisable not to dispense with this idea precipitously in similar cases.

4. K.N., twenty-five years old, single, a small, weakly person of scant intelligence. Has always lived in unfavorable circumstances. Has menstruated since age seventeen. She says she had pneumonia at nineteen, was cared for at home. Since then she has had pains in the chest, difficulty in breathing, and palpitations. Says she had pleuritis in March 1886; was in the Allgemeines Krankenhaus [main Viennese teaching hospital]; says she was jaundiced at the same time. She has been periodically hoarse, sometimes wholly mute since autumn 1886.

She also complains of a stabbing pain in the larynx, especially in the morning. She feels tired, has a stabbing between her shoulder blades, shivering in the morning, and slow but continuous weight loss.

Various means have already been applied to combat the pain in the throat; she has had infusions with astringent medications, electrical treatments that sometimes brought a speedy but transitory improvement in the hoarseness.

Examination on 25 November 1888 reveals an abbreviated sound and unstable breathing in the left upper area as well as at the back of the lung. The laryngoscopic picture shows mild pallor of the mucus of the entire larynx; the vocal chords appear to be somewhat attenuated; at phonation they do not close in the normal way, an elliptical gap remains between them that indicates paresis [partial or incomplete paralysis] of the internal thyroid gland. The attenuation of the vocal chords at first led to the mistaken assumption that therapeutic efforts would meet with little success. When the patient returned a few days later, again totally aphonic, laryngoscopic examination yielded the typical picture of paresis of the inside and transverse areas.

I now hypnotized the patient who was initially very fearful, but who quickly fell asleep. The sensitivity of her skin seemed to be completely gone under hypnosis. I now suggested to her that on waking she would be in full possession of her voice. After a few minutes I woke her. She woke—just as voiceless as before; had lost the headache that had plagued her before, and complained of pain in her left shoulder.

On the next day, 27 November, I again hypnotized her. This time the suggestion made under hypnosis that she would wake in full voice was successful; but the patient came to the Policlinic the next day again aphonic. The laryngoscopic picture was the same as on the day before. I again hypnotized her. She indicates by movements of her head that she understands my words, but cannot answer. I now say to her: "Wake up and speak up!" She opens her eyes, feels a little tired, otherwise well, and answers my questions in a totally normal voice.

On 30 November the patient comes again, not aphonic; however, her voice does not seem as full as last time immediately after hypnosis. In the course of laryngoscopic examination by various gentlemen, she again loses her voice completely. I mention here in parentheses the article by *Boland* (*Verviers*) *Extrait des annales de la société médico-chir. de Liège 1887*, 1887 [Extracts from the Annals of the Medical and Surgical Society of Liège], who cured six cases of hysterical aphonia by suggesting to his patients that the insertion of the laryngoscope would restore their voice.

I hypnotized the patient, suggested return of the voice and paralysis of the right arm. She wakes with an improved but not quite full voice, complains, without being asked, of the weakness in her right arm that she can move only with difficulty. During her hypnotic sleep I had also tried to suggest to her that she could feel everything; nonetheless the previously mentioned anesthesia persisted.

On 3 December the patient came with a voice that sounded rather fuller than last time following hypnosis. The suggestion now made under hypnosis brought further improvement in her voice. This time too her right arm was hard to move when she woke; clearly, under hypnosis the suggestion made the last time had taken effect again, as was likewise observed in another case to be described later.

Only on 9 February, that is after a pause of seventy days, did the patient come to the Policlinic again, maintaining that she had had her voice during this entire time. She complains of pain in the larynx and in swallowing. She is examined by several gentlemen, and in the course of these examinations she once more loses her voice completely. I hypnotize her; she indicates through movements of her head that she understands me but cannot open her mouth to speak. She awakes with a normal voice, feeling very well.

On 11 February she returns, aphonic. She had kept her voice until the previous morning. The pain in her larynx had come back too. Mild catarrh. Paresis of the interior and transverse area. Sensitivity of the mucus wholly maintained. Hypnosis. Absolutely no reaction from her to me in my customary tone; only when I call out in an exceedingly loud voice: "Answer me," does she open her eyes. Her whole body trembles and she says she feels bad. She hides her face in her hands, complains of a headache.

I now hypnotize her while she is lying down. I suggest her voice and the disappearance of the headache. She wakes totally well, speaks loudly, but only for a few minutes—suddenly she is again aphonic. I try suggestion in the waking state: "You can speak." Her voice increases in volume, but does not yet have its normal fullness. It was probably a mistake that I had neglected to determine the length of time she had to retain her voice.

On the next day she comes in the same state in which she had left us on the previous day; in the examining room she again loses her voice. I want to attempt to examine her under hypnosis; she goes into a deep sleep, does not react to me, cannot open her mouth. I experiment with faradaic current. She reacts with muscular movements in her face, in the muscles of her hand without any expressions of pain.

When I apply a somewhat stronger current to her neck, her whole body begins to tremble, she falls off her chair at my feet, and begins to sob loudly without at first being able to utter a word. Then she asks in tears: "Where am I?" I quickly succeed in putting her to sleep again, and suggest to her that she must wake in strong voice, without a headache, and without recalling the past scene. Everything goes according to plan; she wakes feeling completely well, has her voice and no inkling of what had happened in the meanwhile.

Eight days later she comes back with a tolerably good voice. She tells me that she feels very well. This time with good reason; she had in the meanwhile got happily married.

The case described here can hardly be cited as very encouraging proof of the healing power of suggestion in functional aphonia. At any rate, after several sessions success was evident for days and weeks on end. Moreover, the fact that we are dealing with a run-down person with signs of tuberculosis must be taken into consideration. The aphonia was not purely functional, for it also entailed a weakness of certain muscles in the patient's larynx which the influence of suggestion overrode for a while, if such a hypothesis is admissible. It is credible that the weakened muscles could, for hours and days, through psychic influence muster a certain amount of strength normally beyond their capacity. Perhaps marriage can do more than hypnosis was able to do.

5. G.O., a seventeen-year-old girl, rather small and underdeveloped for her age, came to the Policlinic for the first time on 27 February. Her father is healthy, her mother died of a "women's disease," one brother of a lung illness, four siblings are alive. The patient has never had a serious illness. In the summer of the past year she suddenly became aphonic, a condition that disappeared five weeks later just as suddenly as it had appeared. Now she has been without voice for nine weeks.

Examination of the lungs and heart revealed no abnormalities. The laryngoscopic picture was very variable. Within a few minutes, in attempts at phonation, simple paralysis, then a pronounced spasm, and finally signs of a deranged action of the vocal cords could be observed. In addition there was a mild chronic catarrh.

Hypnosis was successful, with the patient falling into a light sleep. I ask her her name, she answers in a completely toneless voice. I say: "Speak up," while at the same time touching her lightly with my hand on her Adam's apple, and she begins to speak more loudly. Repeated suggestions improve her voice from moment to moment until I say to her: "Wake up and speak in a loud voice." She opens her eyes and has a completely normal, sonorous voice. She maintains it for ten days, during which she feels very well; only on the afternoon after the hypnosis she has some pain in the chest. This may have been caused by the effort the patient had made to overcome the spastic aphonia.

On 4 March she had suddenly lost her voice, and came to the Policlinic in a very depressed mood. I tried suggestion in the waking state by simply applying slight pressure to her Adam's apple and saying: "You *can* speak." Her voice then returned completely within a few seconds. Up till now (2 April) no relapse has occurred.

The case is too simple to prompt special reflections. The summary is simply: a weakly girl is aphonic for nine weeks; the first hypnotic suggestion restores her voice; ten days later, renewed aphonia, suggestion in the waking state is effective immediately.

6. A.R., thirty-six years old, married, wife of an official. Her father died of a stroke, her mother of pneumonia; several of the patient's siblings died at an early age, five are still alive. The eldest sister is said to have a chest disease, while another unmarried sister suffers from loss of voice from time to time.

According to her assertion, patient menstruated at age eleven already; later her periods were not totally regular. In her youth she developed very frequent migraines with nausea and vomiting. The patient got married in her nineteenth year, in 1872 and 1877 she bore children, both alive. Seven years ago pneumonia; since then headaches (always on the right side) less violent and frequent. For several years she has often had mild burning pains in the sternum. In spring 1886 the patient suddenly became voiceless, but her voice gradually returned through the use of medications. A year later again loss of voice. Treatment at home, electricity, followed sometimes by a few hours' improvement. In spring 1888 the patient began to cough and lose weight; sometimes blood in the sputum was reported. In summer 1886 her physician diagnosed tuberculosis and ulcers of the larynx; in answer to the patient's questions about her life expectancy, prognosis of at most four months, which she has now very considerably exceeded. Since spring she has been treated with electricity at the Policlinic without the slightest success. At the beginning of October 1888 she was for the first time hypnotized by Prof. *Schnitzler*, whereupon her voice was restored completely—but only for a few hours.

Present condition at the beginning of October 1888: pale, fairly emaciated. On the left tip [of the lung] abbreviated sounds back and front, at the right top abbreviated sound, breathing somewhat shallow, no rattle, heart sounds clear. Mild pain in the ovaries. State of the larynx: at phonation the considerably swollen and red false vocal cords cover the true ones and their front part lies close together; in the back part of the glottis the true vocal cords can be seen partly also lying cramped in a small area. At respiration, quite normal process. Diagnosis: spastic aphonia.

In the middle of October I hypnotized the patient for the first time, using a reflector as I did in my early attempts without since having to resort to it. The headaches, which seem rarely to be absent after this method of hypnosis, can be attributed to the strong irritation of the retina. A few days later, also with this patient, I applied the less harmful method of *Bernheim* mentioned in the introductory lines. After the first hypnotic session her voice returned only for a few hours, later for one or two days. At the beginning I tried to suggest to her the lasting restoration of her voice, but this failed utterly. Suggestion of her voice returning for five or eight days met with no success either. Indeed, it seemed as if the more daring the suggestion of healing, the less its success. If on the other hand I forgot altogether to suggest the length of time the cure would hold, then the voice returned for minutes or for a few hours. Recently I have been proceeding systematically, and gradually a healing of three days can be the aim of a hypnotic session. This is surely a case that must arouse skepticism, but one must take into consideration that the patient is a weak person who suffers from chronic tuberculosis. Moreover, all methods to restore her voice even briefly had failed, while hypnotic suggestion works well; the patiently urgently requests hypnosis that gives her possession of a full, clear voice for at least a few days, and at her special wish I am continuing the treatment that I was more than once inclined to give up because of its minimal success. However, several other happenings are worth mentioning in this patient.

The patient easily falls into deep sleep; yet neither catalepsy nor somnambulism could ever be induced. Under hypnosis complete loss of sensitivity of the skin and the mucus is noted. The patient can never answer the questions put to her, and on waking she has total amnesia. Once I did the experiment of suggesting to her that she would wake without voice. It happened just as I said; she awoke completely aphonic, like she had gone to sleep, and could not understand why this time the hypnosis had had no success. Another time, after I had put her to sleep, she was wakened by another gentleman after I had already made the healing suggestion; she woke aphonic and was unpleasantly surprised at a stranger's participation; at her most pressing insistence I had to hypnotize her again and myself wake her, whereupon her voice returned immediately. If she is hypnotized by other colleagues, the success always holds for just a few hours; this causes her to reject others' attempts—a proof of the medium's habituation to the hypnotizer.

On a few occasions I had succeeded in restoring voice to the totally aphonic patient, though merely a rough voice for a few hours, by touching the false vocal cords with a probe; recently this has not been possible either. During the time of her treatment complete anesthesia of the larynx has developed (not of the epiglottis, which is not rare among hysterics, although it does not occur regularly, as some writers maintain); but as soon as the patient has regained her voice through hypnotic suggestion, the sensitivity is recovered, and the slightest touch of any spot on the laryngeal mucus immediately prompts coughing.

On 8 February the patient returned with a new complaint: on the previous evening she had lost not only her voice but also the power of speech; her tongue was weak, as if paralyzed; at the same time attacks of suffocation had occurred. *Hysterica Mutismus* and *Dyspnoea spastica* [hysterical mutism and spastic shortness of breath]. On the same evening her power of speech, though not her voice, had returned. Hypnosis and suggestion that such attacks should not recur. On that very day it so happened that she was woken out of hypnotic sleep by someone else, woke voiceless, and I had to hypnotize her again in order to bring back her voice. On the evening of that day the previous day's attack was repeated. The next day she entreated me not to let anyone other than me wake her since she believed the recurrence of the attack, despite hypnosis, to have been caused by this circumstance. Hypnosis and healing suggestion. Indeed, neither mutism nor suffocation occurred again.

During the aphonia the patient complains of a bad smell in her nose that disappears as soon as her voice has returned. I recall in this connection the case of H.W., recorded right at the beginning of this report, who thought she could sense a bad smell emanating from her mouth together with the cramplike pains in her larynx. This bore out the coincidence of this olfactory hallucination with the spasticity of the laryngeal muscles.

Finally I still want to mention that in one of the first experiments I carried out with this patient I suggested paralysis of the right arm. After waking the patient could in fact move the arm only with the greatest difficulty and not to the usual extent. "Whatever has happened to my right arm?" she asked anxiously; ever so gradually through persuasion the arm again became movable. After the ensuing hypnotic sessions, the right arm was always reduced in mobility without my having suggested it; in the course of hypnotic sleep the ideas suggested in an earlier hypnosis evidently surface again of their own accord. This symptom disappeared only in time.

In conjunction with the six cases I have here presented let me add that hypnosis did not succeed at all in two further patients with functional aphonia despite repeated attempts. Moreover, I once tried in vain to hypnotize a young lad (a cadet); whether he was influenced or not is open to doubt since the first attempt had to be broken off and no more attempts were undertaken.

I do not feel the right to draw conclusions from the six cases described in the above lines; I prefer simply to depict the impressions I have gained from them. Above all, it appears that as soon as hypnosis is at all successful, functional aphonia can definitely be influenced in a very favorable way.

Only in two of my cases did suggestion not succeed until the second attempt; in the others the first attempt resulted in the immediate restoration of the voice. The dark side of the question is: for how long can the voice be restored? No absolutely certain answer is possible. The duration of success seems dependent on the individual's total condition as well as on the local findings; all sorts of psychic factors undoubtedly play a part, factors so far still beyond our observation. So I would not dare to put the bold word "cured" at the end of any of my cases, although at the moment of this writing almost all my patients appear to be favorably influenced by the suggestive treatment of their aphonia. I would decidedly not wish to see hypnosis and suggestion missing in the future from the therapeutic armamentarium with which we battle functional aphonia. In every case of functional aphonia I would try hypnosis before applying the other very uncertain methods, since hypnosis, if it works at all, restores the sufferer's voice with such amazing rapidity. I recall too the fact that electrical treatment does not ever guarantee a lasting cure for functional aphonia, and I believe that in hypnotic suggestion I also have at my disposal a means to influence favorably certain general neurotic states, of which functional aphonia can be regarded as a symptom.

We can occasionally attain passing successes through hypnotic suggestion even when the sensory or motor disturbances *are not really functional in nature;* if, for instance, we can reduce the pain in an inflamed muscle or to some extent restore its mobility, this seems to rest on the fact that in all pain as well as in a large number of the paralyses that befall part of an organism, there is, as it were, a *residue of functional involvement* of the affected organ that we are able to eliminate through hypnotic suggestion.

NOTES

1. Dagmar C. Lorenz, ed., *A Companion to the Works of Arthur Schnizler* (Rochester, N.Y.: Camden House, 2003).

2. Horst Thomé, ed., *Medizinische Schriften* (Wien and Darmstadt: Paul Zsolnay Verlag, 1988).

3. Sigmund Freud, *Briefe an Arthur Schnitzler,* ed. Henry Schnitzler, *Neue Rundschau* 66, no. 1 (1955): 97; *Letters of Sigmund Freud.* Selected and ed. Frist L. Freud and James Stun (New York: Basic Books, 1960): 339.

4. There is voluminous criticism on this topic. See Furst, "Girls for Sale: Freud's *Dora* and Schnitzler's *Fräulein Else,*" *Modern Austrian Literature* 36, nos. 3/4 (2003).

5. Sigmund Freud. *Gesammelte Werke,* vol. 1, 227 (1904–5): *Standard Edition 1* (London: Imago, 1942), and *Gesammelte Werke,* vol. 1, 227 (1892–95): *Standard Edition 2* (London: Imago, 1942).

6. See Furst, "Anxious Patients/Anxious Doctor: Telling Stories in Freud's *Studies on Hysteria.*" Forthcoming.

4

Jean-Martin Charcot

From the mid- to the later nineteenth century Charcot (1825–93) was the most authoritative figure in what were then known as diseases of the nervous system, a phrase that at that time comprised both neurological and psychiatric disorders. It is no exaggeration to say that he dominated the field as an absolute sovereign; small, stocky, and vigorous, with a large head, he was nicknamed the "Napoleon of the neuroses" because of his resemblance to his military predecessor in behavior as well as in appearance. He enjoyed immense prestige not only professionally but also socially, living in a grand house in Paris, where he gave splendid receptions. On Tuesdays and Fridays he gave lectures; those on Tuesday (the *Leçons du mardi*) were directed at medical students and physicians, while those on Friday, open to the public, attracted large audiences of artists, writers, journalists, intellectuals, and members of high society and became a feature of the Parisian scene. Charcot was so illustrious worldwide that he drew many visitors from other countries, including the then twenty-nine-year-old Freud, who studied with Charcot from October 1885 to February 1886. Freud translated some of Charcot's works and on his death wrote a laudatory obituary of him as the preeminent leader in the field. Freud also named his eldest son Martin in homage to Charcot.

Charcot carried out his work at a hospital for women with the curious name of La Salpêtrière, where he had become chief of the medical service in 1862 at the early age of thirty-seven. Founded in 1656, the hospital was called after the arsenal for the storage of gunpowder (*salpêtre*) that had formerly occupied the same site. When Charcot took over the direction, its population had risen to some five thousand, comprising largely incurables and the insane. Under his reign it was transformed from a custodial hospice into the world's greatest center for clinical research on nervous diseases. Charcot himself described it as a sort of living pathological museum; to him it was a scientific gold mine.

On the occasion of one of the periodic reorganizations of La Salpêtrière, when the renovation of a building required the redistribution of its inhabitants, the epileptics and hysterics were separated from the psychotics. When the new unit was assigned to Charcot, he became intrigued by the tantalizing phenomenon of hysteria, an affliction then associated virtually exclusively with women (see introduction). However, the 1824 *Dictionnaire de médecine* had argued for the existence (but rarity) of hysteria in men.[1] Pierre Briquet, too, in his *Traité clinique et thérapeutique de l'hystérie* (1859) briefly mentions the possibility of male hysteria while again emphasizing its extreme rarity. During the 1830s and 1840s cases were very occasionally recorded in medical journals in Paris.[2] But it was not until Charcot that the presence of hysteria in men began to be acknowledged, albeit still very reluctantly. He himself recorded six cases of male hysteria, one of which is included in this collection. Although Charcot asserted that this is a "rather common case" such as occurred "very frequently in the lower social classes," this is one of the few instances when Charcot's opinion was not widely accepted by physicians. For instance, when Freud, on his return from Paris, gave a lecture on a case of male hysteria to the Viennese Medical Association, he was greeted with derision and disbelieving taunts.

The three cases in this anthology all date from late in Charcot's career, that is, from 1887–88, 1891, 1892. Through his fascination with hysteria, its incidence and popularity increased vastly in scale in France, as is reflected in the number of cases diagnosed as well as in the interest in and knowledge of the malady. It is therefore not surprising that hysteria is Charcot's diagnosis in each of these three instances. Charcot envisaged hysteria as a very widespread disorder about which he formulated distinctive theories such as its schematization into four successive phases that emerge during an acute attack. Thus in the woman with amnesia he points out that her illness follows the "classical sequence" despite the fact that she lacks some of the characteristic symptoms such as pronounced pain in the ovarian region. In the male case, on the other hand, Charcot does ascertain a "hysterogenic zone" in the abdomen. The predominant symptoms are largely in consonance with the prevailing notions of masculine and feminine conduct. The few male patients are more likely to act out physically in disturbances of the five senses, paralysis, headaches, fevers, dizziness, chest pains and palpitations, and language disorders. Their symptoms occur most often in association with a traumatic physical incident or injury as well as in connection with such active behavior as working, drinking, and fornicating to excess. By contrast, the women, as passive victims, talk of labile emotions that they are unable to control.

Charcot concentrates on the physical manifestations of hysteria such as ovarian or abdominal pain, headaches, beating at the temples, because he is a neurologist accustomed to tracking the signs of somatic disease. For most of his life he was convinced that hysteria was an organic disorder that sprang from a lesion seated very likely in the brain or possibly in some other organ, a lesion that would in time be discovered as instruments improved, even if the malady had not yet in his time yielded its secret source. But in the woman with the strange amnesia he argues—and demonstrates—that her memory loss, though hysterical, is purely functional. There is, therefore, a certain amount of contradiction, or at least ambivalence, in his assertions, although predominantly he favored the physiological hypothesis, for Charcot was a distinguished neurologist: he identified multiple sclerosis, tabetic arthropathies, and localized lesions of the spinal cord and described a new clinicoanatomical entity among the progressive muscular atrophies, amylotrophic lateral sclerosis, now known in the United States as Lou Gehring's disease, but initially designated as Charcot's disease in tribute to the precision of his description. His successes in neurology naturally inclined him to search for the somatic sources of hysteria. He very much subscribed to the nineteenth-century belief that research in pathological anatomy was the royal road that would eventually lead to the full understanding of many syndromes including hysteria that still defied medical explanation. This belief was most deeply and early ingrained in France as a result of the pioneering work of Marie-François-Xavier Bichat (1771–1801), whose postmortem dissections ushered in a whole new era in medical research, based on the meticulous observation of a large series of cases from which broad conclusions could logically be deduced. This was the model that Charcot followed in his efforts to achieve a grasp of the processes of hysteria.

Charcot's faith in the validity of the biological model underlies his doubting attitude to psychology, which surfaces repeatedly in these cases. He does not go so far as to dismiss psychology outright, but he is evidently skeptical about venturing into this unknown domain, which was then more closely allied to philosophy than to medicine. Since he was unable to pinpoint the pathological lesion for hysteria, Charcot had to concede that it was perhaps not a purely organic disease. He regarded traumatic shock, either to the body or to the mind, as a causative agent because of the strain it imposes on the nervous system. More than his predecessors, Charcot attributed a major significance to psychic trauma (what he denotes as "moral shock") in the production of hysterical attacks. Yet he also believed in heredity as a major factor implicated in the etiology of hysteria. If the resultant picture is somewhat confused, it is because Charcot himself was undecided; he would have preferred a physical causality as more straightforward and open to proof; however, he had to make concessions and compromises with the possible role of psychological elements.

So in his discussion of the case of amnesia Charcot categorically urges his students not to take "excessive fright at studies that move squarely into psychology." This admonition clearly casts psychology as a troubling and troublesome area. Charcot tries to defuse the "excessive fright" by subsuming psychology into "the realm of medicine," at least "to a certain degree." He argues that it is "nothing but the physiology of the higher or nobler parts of the brain." Thus, even while appearing to defend psychology, Charcot is in effect reducing its status by perceiving it as "nothing but" physiology of the brain. Significantly, in his approach to this case of amnesia, he declares: "I shall limit myself here exclusively to the medical aspect, leaving the psychological aspect aside by choice." In contrasting her total ignorance of recent past events in her waking state with her clear memories under hypnosis, he seems on the verge of admitting the role of the unconscious, but he does not develop this possibility. He leaves psychology totally aside too in the case of the woman with the "hystericotraumatic paralysis." The thought that the woman's paralysis is rooted in her sense of guilt at having slapped her child must surely occur to any post-Freudian reader, especially as her two other children are dead. On the other hand, in the amnesiac Charcot on more than one occasion specifically spells out the important recognition of the simultaneous existence of a conscious self and of unconscious memories that can be recuperated by hypnosis. In the last resort, Charcot's ideas on psychology are patently conflicted and even contradictory as if he wanted to skirt this dangerous terrain by sticking to the seemingly firm ground of somatic medicine. Freud's readiness less than ten years later in his *Studies on Hysteria* to take the risky leap into psychology marks a major watershed in the history of the treatment of nervous afflictions.

Charcot's pronounced preference for somatic medicine over psychology is also determined by his personal predilection for the visual approach. He functioned primarily through his eyes to observe his patients (in contrast to Freud, who used his ears to listen to them). Charcot's lifelong hobby was sketching, and his gift as a caricaturist reveals his capacity to pick out essential characteristics. In collaboration with his colleague Paul Richer, also a talented artist, he edited two volumes, *Les Démoniaques dans l'art* (Demoniac Figures in Art; 1887) and *Les Difformes et les malades dans l'art* (The Deformed and the Sick in Art; 1889). These collected artistic images of epileptics, ecstatics, and hysterics in such varied media as painting, mosaics, tapestries, icons, and bas-reliefs explore the relationship between the visible structures of physical appearance and neurological disorders. In these images, scenes of histrionic spectacle mingle with the medical, as indeed they did in Charcot's lectures and case presentations.

Charcot applied his remarkable visual abilities to his medical practice too in his extraordinarily penetrating powers of observation. In his clinical demonstrations, which became his case histories, he forefronts the impression made by the patient through the act of literally eying her or him. To Charcot seeing the patient did not mean what is normally understood by that term nowadays, that is, an encounter that usually consists, apart from local examination, of dialogue about the patient's complaint(s), the history of the malady's onset, and questions about symptoms. These factors are secondary to Charcot, often relegated to a later part of the discussion of the case. Instead, he puts the primary emphasis on the physician's visual appraisal by means of the most scrupulous notation of every detail of the patient's outer appearance, particularly of any idiosyncrasies or peculiarities indicative of a departure from the norm. He urges his students to be likewise alert to the evidence that can be deduced from such attentive scrutiny. Perhaps it was also this concentration on externals that inhibited Charcot's interest in emotions.

In keeping with this visual bent, Charcot was one of the leaders in the use of photography in medicine. A paper, "On the Application of Photography to the Physiognomic and Mental Phenomenon of Insanity," was read to the Royal Society in London on May 22, 1856, by Hugh W. Diamond, who argued that the photographer can capture in a moment the fleeting facial expressions such as grimaces or fixed stares. This record, which was taken to be perfect and faithful, would enable the physician to witness and to trace the connection between the visible and the invisible.[3] The potential for accessing the invisible through the visible would obviously have strong appeal to Charcot. The appropriation of this new technology into medicine in the mid- to later nineteenth century thus testifies to the faith in the photograph's capacity to supply a reliable source for observation. Charcot established a photographic laboratory at La Salpêtrière in the mid-1880s and appointed Albert Londe, a chemist, to head the service, the first such full-time appointment at any hospital in Europe. Londe's charge was to document the signs and progress of disease by recording its stages on the patient's visible surface in both physiognomy and posture. The focus was on the hysteric's often asymmetrical face, and above all on the eyes, which were regarded as the gateway to the neural network tentatively hypothesized as one of the possible locales of the lesion. The camera therefore came to be perceived as a vital tool for recording pathologies, similar to the histologic cross sections that formed the basis of pathological anatomy. The popularity of photography is confirmed by the series of journals that sprang up in the final quarter of the nineteenth century: the *Revue photographique des hôpitaux de Paris* flourished in the 1870s; it was supplemented by the specialized *Iconographie de La Salpêtrière* 1877–80, which resumed publication in 1888 as the *Nouvelle iconographie de La Salpêtrière.*

While the scrutiny of photographs may have moved the physician closer to the patient in some ways, mainly it had the opposite effect of creating greater distance between them. Charcot's detachment from his patients is also determined by two other important factors. They were without exception lower class, either hospitalized at La Salpêtrière or walk-ins at its ambulatory outpatient clinic. They were thus automatically denied the respect that would be accorded to private, paying patients who consulted a nerve doctor. Arguably with these patients Charcot was forced to rely more heavily on his own visual observations than might have been necessary if his patients had been more educated and articulate. He rarely engages in dialogue with them, and when he does so, he remains very much in control, putting a series of rapid, closed questions, to which he already anticipates the answers. In the case of the amnesiac, the two parallel dialogues serve to structure his presentation and to prove his point that she has lost her memory at only one level because under hypnosis, that is, at another level of consciousness, she is able to retrieve all the details of the past that she appears to have lost.

Charcot's attitude to his patients is further conditioned by their function as teaching material. They are objects for demonstration to students as examples of various syndromes. Charcot is interested in them as specimen types rather than as individuals. He gives just as much personal information about them as is required for an understanding of their illness, for example, that the male hysteric is a cooper, a trade in which alcoholism is rife. He is rather more expansive in regard to the amnesiac, giving her at least an initial, Mrs. D., and a hometown, C. He may have personalized her somewhat more than usual because he considers her case to be "unique," and perhaps because he was flattered by the fact that she had known of him through seeing a famous picture of him hanging in her doctor's office in the provinces. Yet while providing scant social context for his patients, Charcot does insist on their heredity, for, as did most nineteenth-century physicians, he believed in the hereditary predisposition to "nervousness" as a crucial precipitating element in the etiology of mental disorders (see introduction). So he asserts in the case of male hysteria that the "true cause" of the patient's symptoms resides in his nervous heredity rather than in the traumatic accidents he had suffered.

Together with teaching his students and assistants Charcot is concerned too in these cases with what he himself can learn from them. In this period of astonishingly rapid progress in medicine, Charcot is very aware of his role as a pioneer. Although his foremost emphasis is on the patients before his eyes, he never fails to take previous work into account. His case histories are full of scholarly references to the publications of his predecessors and colleagues, some of which he endorses while strenuously contesting or even ridiculing others. Charcot comes across as decidedly autocratic in the firmness, indeed vehemence, of his convictions. Always in command, he makes the impression of needing invariably to be in the right. His fascination with hysteria makes his diagnoses something of a foregone conclusion. On the other hand, despite his arrogance and tremendous self-assurance, he shows himself willing to amend his earlier opinions, notably in regard to male hysteria, where he retracts views he had put forward a mere three years earlier. But he cannot refrain from pointing out that he has at least the satisfaction of knowing that it was his outspoken ideas that prompted precise research into the topic. Even if he was previously mistaken, Charcot has to remain the brightest star in the firmament.

Charcot's scholarly commitment to scientific research far outweighs his interest in therapeutics. Just as readily as he imposes the diagnosis of hysteria, he is wedded to trust in hypnosis and posthypnotic suggestion as the most appropriate treatment (see introduction). He believed that susceptibility to hypnosis indicated the individual's tendency to hysteria, as he mentions in regard to the woman with the paralyzed hand. He devotes surprisingly little attention to the question of therapeutics, merely adding, for instance, "a few words" at the close of the case on male hysteria. Nor does Charcot make much attempt to probe the ulterior psychological causes of his patients' symptoms, as Freud was to do; he is content to deal with the immediate and visible, paying remarkably little attention to his patients' feelings, a facet of psychiatry that has since assumed such a central importance. However, in advocating the separation of the hysterical young girl from her family (at the end of the case on hysterotraumatic paralysis), he does seem to recognize not only the role of feelings but also the possibility of subconscious tensions. By and large he is optimistic about his patients' prognosis, projecting a steady if slow improvement provided they follow his prescriptions by continuing hypnosis and abstaining from self-destructive behavior such as drinking.

In these late cases, Charcot's approach differs from that earlier in his career, when he had believed more strongly in the organic nature of all diseases of the nervous system. Then he and his assistants had experimented with various physical remedies. In the late 1870s and early 1880s they had tried systematic compression of the ovarian region by means of specially devised belts. More conventional treatments such as friction and massage were popular. Chemical substances —ether, amyl nitrate, bromides, chloroform, and morphine—had proved unsuccessful. With Charcot's consent, members of his team experimented with their favorite methods, notably electrotherapy and metallotherapy, which consisted of the application of copper, silver, or iron bars. A report on metallotherapy to the Société de Biologie in 1877 claimed that it undoubtedly provoked a cerebral action. Though actually ineffective in itself, it was metallotherapy that led Charcot to hypnosis, whose power was thought to stem from the transfer of forces from one person to another as from metal to human being. Clearly, the idea of being able to control and remediate another person was likely to appeal to a domineering personality such as Charcot's. By the time of these three late cases hypnosis had become the standard, indeed almost the exclusive method for him.

Charcot's manner of presenting his cases was another channel for the assertion of his power. Instead of adopting the normative method of writing up accounts to be read by individuals in private, Charcot opted to give public lectures, "lessons," as he called them. Speaking more or less improvisationally in the first person, Charcot's mode is vigorous and colloquial to the point of casualness, certainly in the context of his time, when formality was the rule. In contrast to the custom in medical discourse that rested on objective, impersonal statements, Charcot favors the unconventionally personal. He uses a lot of rhetorical questions as if engaging in dialogue with his audience. What is more, the very word *lesson* projects a master/subordinate relationship. Both the Tuesday and the Friday series are overtly addressed to an audience present as recipients of his utterances. These lectures were recorded by his assistants, who acted as scribes. The Tuesday lessons often open formally with "Gentlemen," and Charcot frequently resorts to the direct address in the second person plural, *you* (*vous*), to confirm the teaching situation as he admonishes students to pay particular attention to certain distinctive features of the patient under consideration. Sometimes he engages playfully in pseudo-dialogues as he imputes to his listeners hypothetical objections, which he quickly dispels. The give-and-take is only apparent, for it is always Charcot who does all the giving. Equally deceptive is the semblance of the lessons' associative, digressive structure, which is, of course, a result of their origin in spoken delivery. However, though Charcot makes detours, he never loses sight of his ultimate goal of interpreting the case and skillfully returns to his main thread as he focuses once more on the day's patient.

Charcot's ability consistently to draw large audiences of lay people, which confirms contemporary reports of him as a spellbinding speaker, is also due to his brilliance in the handling of communicative language. He shows a gift that transcends the scientific in his introduction of vivid images; for example, in the case of the woman with the hystericotraumatic paralysis he compares various aspects to a muff, to rose water, to a mushroom, and hypnosis to a parasite, thereby grounding his medical observations in the sphere of the down to earth that would help to familiarize the bewildering phenomena he describes. His underlying tactic is therefore to counteract the estrangement his patients' behaviors would unavoidably elicit; bizarre though they are, he endeavors if not to domesticate them, at least to tame them to some extent by drawing them not only within the forum of medicine but also toward the domain of the knowable. He thus steers a tricky course between acknowledging his patients' peculiarities and accommodating them within the parameters of human experience. Charcot's striking, occasionally flamboyant rhetoric differentiates his case histories from the more sober written accounts of his contemporaries (e.g., Krafft-Ebing and Schnitzler) even when they were reporting pathologies as grave and grotesque as those of the French master.

Reading Charcot's case histories underscores the extent to which he was essentially both a storyteller and a showman. As Freud would later, he produces narratives that are tales of detection: the subject of the mystery is the patient's disorder, which the doctor as the perspicacious detective proves able to decipher through a combination of hypermeticulous observation, extraordinary knowledge, penetrating insight, logical deduction, and a smattering of intuition. The starting point is formed by the perplexing symptoms, which Charcot catalogs in great detail and with evident relish. He enjoys startling his audience and arousing their curiosity, which he, with his superb understanding of the syndrome, will in the end be able to satisfy. The disposition of the narrative material is literary, or perhaps more precisely, oratorical, as Charcot alternates between the chronological sequence in tracing the unfolding of the patient's illness and excursions into the past to fill in the background and oblique glances into the future as he hints at revelations he will later make. Through this manipulation of time, Charcot cleverly builds up the suspense as listeners become increasingly intrigued by what can be called the plot and increasingly avid to hear its outcome. As the discourse progresses, Charcot becomes a sort of medical Hercule Poirot, who sees more than others, commands deeper insight, and can by an amalgam of logical ratiocination and inspired moments of illumination provide the key to the mystery that is beyond the grasp of the ordinary listener. Charcot thus features as the hero of his case histories able to rescue his patients from their imprisonment in their hysteria by means of hypnosis.

Charcot's presentations of his case histories therefore take the form of performances, not only in their spoken format but also in the entire theatrical atmosphere he created. As Elisabeth Bronfen has so aptly summarized it, Charcot's case histories are a "staging of his own phantasm of omnipotence."[4] That lust for omnipotence was certainly sensed by his patients. The suspicion has been raised that some of his hysterical women patients were in collusion with these performances. From helping his scribes to copy their notes, they knew of the sequence Charcot expected in their attacks, and it has been suggested that they may deliberately have simulated the successive stages so as to please him. At certain high points the patients under discussion were taken before the audience as the centerpiece and climax of the spectacle to be demonstrated, and sometimes they were questioned, although the questioning is less a genuine interrogation than a confirmation of what Charcot already knew. The most dramatic example of the impact of direct questioning occurs in the amnesiac woman, who can give no answers at all in her current pathological condition, yet who can respond with perfect recall under hypnosis. The crass contrast between her untreated and her treated state is a most effective way for Charcot to parade the power of hypnosis and concomitantly his own power.

Charcot's case histories are without parallel. His gifts for observation, for oratory, and not least for showmanship are quite unique. His individuality is so pronounced that he was not a model who could be followed by either his contemporaries or his successors. He reached beyond the limits of conventional medical discourse to fashion case histories that remain highly readable today. Despite some undeniable shortcomings in his beliefs and methods, Charcot has to be hailed as the luminary he was in his own day.

A HYSTERICO-TRAUMATIC PARALYSIS
LEÇONS DU MARDI, 1887–88, 111–18

A woman came to see me; I saw her for only a moment, she had experienced a strange accident which will not be difficult to interpret today, but which would be almost incomprehensible if we were not familiar with the field.

About a year ago she gave a slap to her seven-year-old son. This is not a rarity in a certain environment, but what is much rarer is that it has left her with a special kind of paralysis of her hand, a paralysis less pronounced today than earlier, but still recognizable, and, I repeat, dating back a year. The blow was given by the back of the hand. There are at least two kinds of blows: those given by the palm of the hand placed against the cheek one wants to strike, others given by the back of the hand.

You will perhaps say: what the devil kind of blow could this woman have dealt her child for it to have left her with a paralysis that has persisted for a year. The child fell over, so the blow was terrific. Not at all, it seems that the blow was not very violent. The kid didn't cry more than is normal after a well aimed slap, and the husband, who was present, was most astonished to see its effect not on the child, but on the mother. It is she who suffered most. Almost immediately she felt something special in her hand and had difficulty in moving and extending it.

Here is an apparently insignificant happening; nevertheless it must prompt all sorts of reflections in an attentive physician.

Someone comes to consult you about paralysis of the hand. This isn't the first time that accidents of this kind are seen following an absolutely mild trauma, and presently I will cite you some examples.

Here then is a mild traumatic accident that is in reality not at all serious but that nonetheless needs to be examined because it results in a functional disturbance of movement. How did these things happen?

I say that this paralysis affects above all the movement of extension. (*To the patient*) Stretch out your hand.

As you can see, she stretches out her hand, and if you try to bend it, she offers no kind of resistance; you can easily see that. On the other hand, in flexion there is a certain resistance. This was much stronger; only a vestige of it still remains.

But note that it is a year since the accident occurred. In regard to sensitivity, the effects are very marked.

If you consider the cutaneous sensitivity and then the distribution of this sensitivity, when it is the nerves that are affected, you get anesthesia in areas corresponding to the distribution of these nerves.

A few days ago in a patient suffering from a sciatic lesion I showed you one of these anesthetic areas.

The radial and the cubital nerves are distributed cutaneously. Consequently, if these nerves were affected, you would have that kind of distribution, but that isn't the case at all; it's an anesthesia terminated by an amputation line. It forms a sort of muff. At the same time there has been a profound anesthesia of sensitivity and a more or less complete loss of muscular sense so that when her fingers are moved, she doesn't really know which finger has been touched.

Those who have kept up with new studies of this type of affliction will have guessed what it is. There are only two questions that have to be put: what is the cause of this anesthesia, this partial loss of movement in the fingers, for the dynamometer shows a considerable difference, even in the least affected part?

Is it a cerebral lesion? Only a cortical lesion can give rise to anesthesias of this kind. They cannot come from a spinal lesion nor from a bulbar lesion nor from a lesion of the central membranes; it has to be the cerebral cortex. It is in the cortex that the seat of paralyses of this kind resides. However, there is only one malady that produces these accidents, and that is hysteria. This woman is a hysteric on account of the kind of distribution of her anesthesia and the kind of loss of movement she has experienced. She therefore has a cortical lesion, but it isn't an organic lesion. It is neither a softening, nor a bleeding, nor any other gross material lesion following a slap given by her to her child; it's a dynamic lesion. We already have some idea of this type of traumatization, and I am convinced that I can reproduce it in persons who have major hysteria and who would at the same time be eminently susceptible to hypnotism.

When you have hypnotized one of these patients, if you command her to give a slap, she will do it and you can at your will produce the phenomena we observe in this woman: the hand placed in the position you see, the difficulty in extending it, a more or less complete cutaneous anesthesia with a profound anesthesia of the fingers, consequently a faithful reproduction of what nature offers us without hypnotism. This has been established and demonstrated with certainty, and I will give you a performance of it one of these days on a subject on whom the experiment can be carried out. You will see this artificial paralysis resulting from the reproduction of the action of the slap except that the subject will be placed in a special state, which will not be that of an angry woman.

What matters is to find out whether there is an analogy between the two states. Those eminently susceptible to hypnosis are hysterics, and I will show you that this woman is eminently hysterical.

Is the mental state of a hysterical woman seized by anger similar to that of a woman highly susceptible to hypnosis who is put into a somnambulistic state?

Yes indeed! There is an extraordinary analogy between the two states. In both cases suggestion is involved. In the angry hysterical woman, the suggestions are very facile—not the suggestions from outside imposed on her by the experimenter, but those produced naturally.

It is merely a matter of demonstrating how it can happen that the particular feeling that produces the action of giving a slap can result in a complete loss of sensitivity and a complete loss of movement, things that are in total an exaggerated reproduction of the mild loss of movement in the hand when it comes up against a hard body.

For it is important to note that when you give a slap, even a mild slap, you feel a kind of numbing in the hand and if you take a dynamometer you will see that if you hit a little too hard, a certain temporary anesthesia ensues; surgeons know this well. Dr. Grenier has designated this phenomenon with the name local shock, and Dr. Bilbroth tells how he had felt such a local shock after striking himself a blow.

You have a special kind of numbness and perhaps some anesthesia that you may perhaps be able to ascertain if you seek it out. This woman is telling you that she first had paralysis of movement and of sensitivity; she probably felt local shock when she dealt her blow. And I am telling you that we know very well from experience that local shock is more pronounced in some people than in others following the same traumatic action. For example, let a robust countryman strike himself: the feeling that he will experience will be slight, but take a nervous woman, the feeling will be stronger, and much stronger still in the hysteric. The local shock must therefore have been stronger in this woman than in anyone else.

I told you that the mental state of a hysterical woman is very analogous to that of those who are hypnotized.

What is the mental state in somnambulism?

An absolute absence of reaction, an idea that penetrates the interior of the brain like a parasite. It lodges there without competition from other ideas; they are absent; everything is asleep. It's the same in the case before us. An idea comes from outside, an impression, the phenomena stemming from the shock. Now these phenomena are introduced into the covering of the brain under special conditions when everything is asleep except what you wake, and what is then woken are precisely the ideas connected to the absence of movement and the disturbance of sensitivity. And not only does this develop to an intense degree, but it also persists. It is the jolts that persist. You know how sometimes when you have put a subject to sleep and introduced an idea into their mind, not only is that idea dominant during sleep, but it persists on waking because it has been implanted without the competition of other ideas and becomes imposed like a kind of dream.

According to certain modern psychologists, according to Herbert Spencer, Bain, the thought of a deed is already an accomplished deed; when we think of the movement of extending our hand, we already sketch the movement of extending the hand so that if the idea is forceful, we carry it out.

You must realize too that the idea of the absence of movement, the lack of power, becomes fact in like manner, and that is how things happen in regard to movements and ideas. It is the idea become fact, obviously corresponding to a modification in certain cortical regions. It's as clear as daylight; there is no idea that does not have an essential substratum in the mind. When the idea of absence of movement comes to dominate, paralysis can result from it.

My explanation perhaps seems difficult and far-fetched to you. I understand that a grasp of it demands more or less in-depth studies that are not within everyone's reach. It might perhaps be necessary to apply oneself a little, for as far as nervous maladies are concerned, psychology plays a part, and what I call psychology is the rational physiology of the cerebral cortex.

But let's admit that the explanation may not be clear to you. Yet it is an experimental fact. I told you that we can reproduce this paralysis in all its aspects.

So, let's say that this woman is a hysteric. Perhaps we should demonstrate this more completely. That isn't difficult. The other day, in examining her, we found on her what we will call stigmata. There is no anesthesia, no loss of the tongue's special sensitivity, no reduction of the visual field. Neither the general nor the special sensitivity is affected. But in the last resort these stigmata are not absolutely crucial. And here we have a dominant symptom, namely that determined by the trauma. But there's something else; there's the ovary, commonly involved in attacks of hysteria. We saw the other day: she gave us a performance of one of these attacks under the influence of emotion, with whistling in the throat, throbbing in the temples, buzzing in the ears. What does she have? A whole past and a heritage that reveal many things.

This woman comes from Nîmes. She is thirty-one, has had three children. It's the eldest who got the slap.

> (*Speaking to the patient*): Where are the others?
> *The patient:* They are dead.
> *Dr. Charcot:* She is violent in her household. It is said that the child had to be removed because he was given too many blows.
> *The patient:* That wasn't the reason. It was because he was constantly sick.
> *Dr. Charcot:* In any case he is more protected from that kind of trauma since he has been removed from the parental home. Is he with you at present?
> *The patient:* Yes, sir.
> *Dr. Charcot:* She is very lively, easily angered, and you know that southerners of her sort are not patient. What is more, there are pathological antecedents; you cannot hold that against her. Heredity is interesting because it always brings us back to the same principle: it proves that hysteria doesn't appear out of nowhere like a mushroom.

Here is the information that has been gathered:

> *Father, sixty-four years old:* joint pains and kidney stones.
> *Mother:* died of heart disease, had joint pains.

So much for arthritis.

Here now is the nervous side:

Grandfather on the maternal side was an epileptic.

That is her heredity; it is of some importance, as you can judge. Since childhood she has shown the special tendencies which have now come so strongly into play. She has menstruated since thirteen; she was well until the age of eighteen, when she had her first accident. She lived near Nîmes. An agricultural machine was going through her village; suddenly the driver gave out a sharp whistle that she wasn't expecting, and she went into an attack of sleep which was followed by a series of others in the next two years. She was woken only to eat. You know that such attacks are quite simply transformed hysterical attacks. So: heredity, attacks of sleep, genuine hysterical attacks involving the ovary; that's her past, then, one fine day, after a slap given in a bout of anger, a special type of paralysis. This is totally characteristic of hysteria; nothing surprising; only the question of treatment remains. She must be cured of her attacks of nerves and at the same time of what is left of this sort of paralysis, and that isn't altogether easy, all the more so as she wants to stay at home. She will come to take a series of treatments by static electricity. Also, since hysteria is nearly always combined with anemia and chlorosis, she will take iron and will stay calmly and quietly at home.

It's easy to advise a patient to stay calm, but you know the importance of isolation in cases of this type; if her husband and her children weren't there, it might be possible. There should be some sort of institutions where hysterics could be isolated. Unfortunately, there aren't any. It can't even be done here. These patients are, on the contrary, side by side. However, they are maybe better off here than at home, because the husband and the children aren't there; there's no need to work, to be preoccupied with subsistence for all of them. That's worth something, but in the last resort we can't give them perfect isolation. That's possible only for wealthy patients. There are in fact four large hydropathic institutes in Paris, where we can practice on a large scale; therefore hysterics are numerous there.

In order properly to treat a hysterical young woman she should not be left with her father and her mother; she should be put into a rest house where she would be allowed to come into contact only with a person experienced in this kind of treatment, and under the direction of a doctor who oversees that she is handled as she should be.

It's a kind of voluntary sequestration. Then what was difficult becomes easy, but I would never advise a doctor to undertake such cures while leaving the hysteric at home

What is the use of potassium bromide? None. The magnetic iron ore displaces sensitivity, the local accident, but you will not cure the diathesis [constitutional tendency to certain diseases] underlying it. Isolation necessary for cure will always be lacking within the family, the more so as the family itself is generally hysterical and the coincidence of the two hysterias merely accentuates them.

Often, when I preach the necessity for this separation of a hysterical girl from her family I encounter the objection that a young girl cannot be separated from her mother; then I reply that this may be true in novels, but that in reality things happen differently. It is indeed curious to see how hysterics change from one day to the next. When a young hysterical girl is separated from her mother, the spectacle is very moving, but suddenly she resigns herself to it with the greatest ease. How many times have I seen this change. So when a mother comes and says to me: How do you expect this girl who has never left me to be separated from me?, I reply: I know this story. Do you know how many times well brought up young girls weep for their mothers when they leave them? I have taken notes. There are some who do not weep at all; that's a fact; others weep for an hour; let's take the average, if you like; it's half an hour; that isn't much. Yet I cannot give a lesson in the psychology of hysteria to all the mothers who come with their children. And I know that I am not at all understood in this point because I know only too well that psychology has not yet merged with physiology. Up to now it has been customary to set psychology aside, it's taught in college, but that's a minor psychology in rose water that doesn't do much good. To know that we have differing faculties doesn't have much practical application. Another kind of psychology must be created, a psychology supported by the pathological studies to which we are devoting ourselves. We are in the process of doing this in cooperation with psychologists, who, this time, really want to take into consideration not just what is called inner observation, as did their predecessors. Former psychologists used to shut themselves up in their study, look inwards, and be their own subjects of observation. It was a method that could be useful but that was totally inadequate. For controlled observation of man by himself, there must be a reverse observation, and in this reverse observation the pathology of the nerves plays a considerable role.

NOTES

1. Jan Goldstein, "The Uses of Male Hysteria: Medical and Literary Discourse in Nineteenth-Century France." *Representations* 34 (Spring 1991): 135 (134–65).
2. Goldstein, "The Uses of Male Hysteria," 151.
3. See Sander L. Gilman, *Faces of Madness* (New York: Brunner/Mazel, 1976), 20–24.
4. Elisabeth Bronfen, *The Knotted Subject: Hysteria and Its Discontents* (Princeton, N.J.: Princeton University Press, 1998), 193.

SALPÊTRIÈRE HOSPITAL
"ON A CASE OF MALE HYSTERIA"

1. DISSOCIATED PARALYSIS OF THE LOWER FACE,
OF HYSTERICAL ORIGIN

2. ACCUMULATION OF ETIOLOGICAL FACTORS:
TRAUMA, ALCOHOLISM, HEREDITY OF NERVOUSNESS.

LESSON RECORDED BY GEORGES GUINON,
HEAD OF THE CLINIC

ABSTRACT: Progress made in the knowledge of male hysteria in France and abroad.—Description of a case of facial paralysis of hysterical origin affecting only the buccinator and large zygomatic muscles.—Superposition of anesthesia and paralysis.—Diversity of opinions concerning the existence of facial paralysis in hysteria. Its relative rarity compared to hysterical glosso-labial spasm.
In this case onset of the neurosis on the occasion of a trauma, and of the facial paralysis on the occasion of another trauma undergone in an assault.—The role of these agents in the development and evolution of nervous accidents: accumulation of precipitating agents.

Gentlemen,
The patient I'm going to present to you today is quite simply a male hysteric. It is therefore on the whole a rather commonplace case. For, as you know, thanks to the efforts of the French school, male hysteria, whose great frequency daily arouses astonishment, has assumed an important place in the clinical work of the Parisian hospitals, where this type of patient has been examined and welcomed. Thus, through the introduction of this new guest, the neuropathological

domain has been profoundly transfigured, surely for the greatest good of the patients and the doctors: for the patients, who instead of being rejected as worthless, often as feigners, are willingly accepted and appropriately cared for; for the doctors, who are no longer liable to commit always regrettable injustices toward these unhappy creatures by mistreating them or failing to recognize their afflictions, and who, because they are better versed in the field, no longer risk, as formerly, making mistaken diagnoses all the time by taking for an organic lesion a malady that is not such, and vice versa.

Is it necessary to remind you of the numerous works that have recently appeared on this subject to support what I have just said? Let me just mention a few. I would refer you first to the article by the former head of my clinic, Dr. P. Marie, currently a clinical professor and member of the Faculty. He has compiled statistics of the cases of hysteria he encountered while he was consultant to the Central Board and was able to see male hysteria very frequently in the lower social classes; it seems even to be more frequent there than female hysteria. We are dealing here, of course, with major hysteria, compulsive hysteria, as Dr. Marie calls it, for as far as mild hysteria is concerned, the situation is rather the opposite.

Think also of the work of Dr. Souques, my current assistant, who examined all the cases of male hysteria that turned up in one recent year in the wards of the Broussais hospital in Dr. Chauffard's department. He shows that in a ward of thirty-two patients twenty-six male hysterics had been seen in one year. His work leads to the same conclusions as Dr. Marie's.

In addition I will cite here the oral reports given many times by many of my hospital colleagues that can be summed up as follows: formerly we used not to see male hysteria; nowadays it surfaces constantly in considerable proportions. How many times have I heard my colleagues speak of this?

Other documents also show us that in the provinces things do not differ from Paris in this respect provided that the available observational material is sufficient. So Dr. Bitot at Bordeaux has observed within two years over twenty cases of male hysteria solely in the general clinic directed by Professor Pitres.

I am not discussing other countries where conversion "to male hysteria considered as a frequent malady of manual workers" is under way. In England the work of the Manchester school has contributed much to further the issue thanks to the studies of Drs. Dreschfeld, Thornburn, and Page, to name just a few. In Germany, at least in

Berlin, there is hardly any essential difference of opinion between our colleagues and us. Professor Mendel has shown the frequency of hysteria in men in that city's policlinics. Dr. Oppenheim's observations on traumatic neuroses do not differ fundamentally, I think, from our own, and it is at present legitimate, if I am not mistaken, to subsume under the aegis of hysteria a goodly number of cases designated as traumatic neuroses. I see no objection to the application of this denomination if it is agreed that it is taken to refer most often to male hysteria that does not differ essentially in symptoms and prognosis from male hysteria stemming from other causes.

In the smaller centers in Germany the field seems less advanced. It is clearly necessary to have at our disposal a large amount of clinical material, both general and special, in order to observe male hysteria on a daily basis.

It requires in fact special conditions for it to develop and spread. Its victims are mainly proletarians engaged in a difficult daily struggle for survival, the ill-fated, the disinherited. Alcoholism, toxic trades, traumas play a big role, without taking nervous heredity into account. In the smaller centers this unquestionably does not hold to the same extent so that sometimes, doubts seem to arise about the validity of observations gathered elsewhere although they are quite undisputable. What has not been, what has not been touched, is not believed. That's the doctrine of skepticism in all its severity. This has its good side, to be sure, but it mustn't be taken to extremes, to disbelief in the positions taken. Do we Parisians believe in the existence of leprosy, beriberi, yellow fever, and other exotic maladies although these are afflictions that most of us have never seen? We believe in them very firmly, however, on the strength of the critical examination we have been able to make of the documents on which knowledge of these cases is based. It should be the same for male hysteria. Let those who are not well placed to see it get to know it from those who observe it daily on a large scale. I can see no better way of doing it.

So it is not without astonishment that I recently saw a most distinguished neuropathologist write the following in an otherwise very interesting paper on traumatic neurosis:

"Let us not take these neuroses (traumatic neuroses), especially hysterical neuroses too seriously. The doctor can often contribute to spreading hysteria and making it an epidemic illness. *Above all let us not coddle hysteria in men too much; let's leave it to women and children.*" These proposals certainly contain much "humor"; but what strikes us most is the reflection of a foregone attitude, of a resolve taken a priori that will perhaps make the truly scientific appreciation of the clinical facts more difficult. Let us wait patiently for the light to dawn in this quarter; it will come.

But I don't want to tarry longer on the preliminaries; I come to our patient. Again, I don't present him to you as anything extraordinary. All in all, as I said, it's a banal case; however, as you know, careful examination almost always turns up some new point, some unexpected combination even in the simplest, most commonplace cases. Seen from this perspective, our case will arouse interest.

It does indeed present a well demonstrated, authentic example of *hysterical facial paralysis,* the existence of which had until recently seemed very problematic to me. The paralysis, which affects the lower part of the face, is no doubt slight but still genuine. So that it doesn't feature twice in the annals of medicine, I hasten to inform you that this case of hysterical facial paralysis is the same as that presented by Dr. Ballet to the *Société médicale des hôpitaux* [Hospitals' Medical Association] at its meeting on 24 November 1890. It is thanks to Dr. Ballet's cooperation that I have got to know it and can examine it with you.

I will remind you in a moment how the question of facial paralysis in hysterics has been perceived and how until recently this affliction, which seems to be quite rare, was open to doubt or even formally negated by a group of observers, of which I had the honor of being a member, but from which I must now dissociate myself, although not unconditionally.

The case is interesting from another point of view too. It shows us how in the production of male hysteria there can be, as it were, an accumulation of precipitating factors, as Dr. Georges Guinon, my chief assistant, has so rightly pointed out in his work on the precipitating factors in hysteria. Heredity is definitely one element in the majority of cases, but several precipitating factors vie for primacy. The advocates of symptomatic hysteria would have a good time making it a case of toxic hysteria; alcoholic habits are indeed deeply ingrained in our patient. Other proponents of multiple hysterias will also object with good reason, since it isn't alcohol that brought on the first attack and revealed the hysteria but a trauma, or rather, for there was neither a wound nor a mechanically caused concussion, a nervous shock, a fright; they identified in it all the traits of traumatic hysteria, which they wanted, wrongly, to turn into a separate illness under the name of traumatic neurosis.

In reality nothing is more apt than this combination of different precipitating factors to demonstrate, as I have been maintaining for a long time, that hysteria is singular and indivisible, and that its true cause lies not in the fortuitous influences that bring it out, but rather in the predisposition created by a heredity of nervousness.

But before going into the various points I have just enumerated, I want to study the patient clinically and acquaint you with his current status.

He's a lad of twenty-four, called Bar . . . , a cooper, alas! a trade that has contributed significantly to his downfall and in which he has picked up the destructive habits that make his cure so difficult. We admitted him to the Salpêtrière in February 1891 from Dr. Proust through the intermediacy of Dr. Ballet. His condition is the same today as it was on his admission. He is rather a slender lad, yet well built, otherwise healthy, apart from slight anemia.

He was sent to us as a hysteric, and it didn't take us long to recognize first the presence of typical convulsive attacks, characteristic of major hysteria, with large circular movements, etc. These attacks are never accompanied by tongue biting: they last up to half an hour. He has had them about every eight to ten days, almost without fail, every time he leaves the hospital to do errands in town as a result of the liquor which he unfortunately never fails to imbibe on these occasions.

Moreover, more or less pronounced hysterical stigmata provided a further basis for the diagnosis. First, there is absolute anesthesia to touch, temperature, and pain, whose distribution is extremely interesting. It is localized on the right in that part of the lower face that can be called the cheek, comprises the chin, and extends inward on the corresponding side to the mucus of the buccal cavity. We shall later see the reason for this disposition of the anesthesia that can at first glance appear to be peculiar.

There is no other area of anesthesia, but in the hypochondrium [abdomen] on the left side the presence of a perfectly characteristic hysterogenic zone is to be noted.

Finally we note the existence of a double narrowing of the visual field with micromegalopsy in both eyes, without a central scotoma. Taste, hearing, and smell are attenuated on the left side. The pharyngeal reflex is totally gone on the same side. There is no sign of hemiplegia [paralysis of one side of the body] in the limbs.

Sleep is restless, often broken by nightmares that consist mainly of the feeling of falling into a precipice. He assures me that he has never seen animals in his dreams. At night he also often suffers from violent cramps in his legs and tingling in his feet and hands. But this goes beyond the realm of hysteria and derives more likely from alcoholism.

Now I want to dwell on the features of the facial paralysis that I have mentioned to you.

At rest a certain amount of asymmetry is readily visible. The left labial commissure [angle or corner of the eye or lip] seems drawn slightly upward and outward, while the right droops. There is no abnormality of the tongue. But if the patient is made to laugh or to grimace, the left commissure is seen to rise noticeably and to be surrounded by folds in a semicircle.

On the right, the muscles of the chin and of the lower lips function normally. The same holds for the spreading movement of the commissure on the horizontal level, for the raising of the upper lip, and for the closing of the lips and whistling. But the commissure's movement outward and upward does not take place and we know in addition that the cheek muscle was once paralyzed because the patient has told us that he used to be obliged to lift with his fingers food that was falling into the gingival channel. So only two muscles seem to be affected: the cheek and the large zygomatic muscle.

Let me add that the electromuscular reactions are perfectly normal despite the fact that the paralysis has gone on for about three years, and there is no trace of muscular spasms or shaking.

Here then is a clearly noted paralysis in a hysteric, one that seems to me to devolve from hysteria. I need now to bring out all the interest inherent in this case, and in order to do so, I must investigate matters a little further.

In 1856, in a paper on hysterical paralysis Todd wrote the following lines: "The extent of the paralysis of the limbs, when there is no trace in the face, is an argument in favor of the hysterical nature of the affliction: for although hysteria may appropriate all the parts of the trunk and of the limbs, very rarely, perhaps never, does it invade the face."

So hysterical hemiplegia does not generally attack the face, perhaps it never attacks the face itself: that is Todd's opinion, and it is shared by Hasse, Althaus, and more recently Weir Mitchell in accordance with their personal observations. I adopted the same view and the same formula. So in a lesson published in the *Semaine médicale*

[Medical Weekly] of 2 February 1887 I said: "In hysterical hemiplegia the lower face is never involved on the paralyzed side in a manner comparable to ordinary hemiplegia."

It's not that a deviation of the face called paralysis has not been noted in several publications in opposition to the formula proposed by Todd and others. But if you look more closely, you often find in these cases the characteristics of a spasmic, not a paralytic deviation. The tongue is most often twisted, rolled around itself, and the patient can't move it out of his mouth. That is the situation in the case published by Dr. Strassmann under the title of facial hemiplegia in hysteria. In this patient the tongue is rolled around itself, its tip fixed on the top of the palate. There is in addition a certain degree of trismus [lockjaw]; the teeth are clenched, the head is turned to the left. Perhaps this is a manifestation of right-sided facial paralysis? I would assert this of Lebreton's earliest case where hemiplegia of the limbs and total facial paralysis on one side are said to have occurred. When subjected to scrutiny, it does not prove convincing.

Thus, gentlemen, my opinion used to be that facial deviations superposed on hysterical hemiplegia were the consequences of a unilateral glottolabial spasm, that appropriated at times the opposite side to the hemiplegia, at other times the same side. This spasm, which we have just noted and which furnished the explanation of facial deviations in hysterical hemiplegia, was duly noted in 1888 by Drs. Brissaud and Marie. They showed all its characteristics to perfection, the traction of the commissure, the twisting of the tongue, the possible extension to the realm of the upper face, the muscular shakings that accompany it, etc., etc.

Quite recently, in 1888, in my *Leçons du mardi* [Tuesday Lessons] (I:299) I wrote: "As long as it has not been shown that hysterics' facial paralyses are not partial spasms, I shall persist in my negation, though ready to surrender in case the facial paralysis, whose existence in hysteria I contest for the moment, should become well and duly shown."

Today, you see that I have to surrender. I do so without hesitation or bitterness, for at least I have the satisfaction of having confronted the issue squarely and of having, by my outspoken view, provoked precise research on this point of nervous pathology. The results of this research, without being as yet very numerous, have however recently appeared in various publications, particularly in the important papers of the *Société médicale des hôpitaux* [Hospitals' Medical Association] of 1890 and 1891. They establish that facial paralysis is an exceptional occurrence in hysteria; it is unusual in its manifestations; often differing in several aspects from organic hemiplegia, it can nonetheless present in such a way as to make it more difficult than one might think to achieve a differential diagnosis between capsular and hysterical hemiplegia.

Dr. Ballet, at the beginning of 1890 already, approached the question by presenting a patient. Some time later Dr. Chantemesse published three cases of hysterical facial paralysis in men with brachial monoplegia. He pointed out that in all the cases the paralysis is not pronounced and that there is always marked and sometimes predominant anesthesia in the paralyzed face and limbs. This is an important feature in contrast to what usually happens in organic hemiplegia.

In this connection I remind you that Dr. Gilles de la Tourette, when he was my assistant, already published a paper on the superposition of disturbances of sensitivity in the face and the neck in hysterics. His work concerns spasms, not paralyses; but the two groups of facts must obviously be considered as belonging to the same series. They cannot be wholly separated.

Then finally Dr. Ballet's case, which refers to the same patient as I am presenting to you today, was soon followed by another example of the same kind from Dr. Bonnet. So that makes five cases from trustworthy, competent authors, well versed in the field, and particularly knowledgeable about the deviations that glossolabial spasms can produce in hysterics.

Five recorded cases is admittedly still little; but it's already something and at any rate we are forced today to recognize that in the great majority of cases facial paralysis does not accompany hysterical hemiplegia, but that sometimes it can do so.

Please note that as of now paralysis of the lower face in a hysteric seems to be distinguished by certain features from those found in the corresponding organic hysterical hemiplegia. First of all it is generally very little pronounced. Second, it always seems to be accompanied by anesthesia of the paralyzed parts, as Dr. Gilles de la Tourette already noted in regard to spasms. Finally, it has several times been recorded quite separately from any evident paralysis of the limbs, a circumstance seldom found in the history of capsular facial hemiplegia and represented in the class of cortical paralyses by very rare cases.

Thus everything is in place and from now on it's a matter of researching under what circumstances either hysterical facial paralyses or deviations of spasmodic origin are produced.

Perhaps this is the place to remind you that facial hysterical paralyses do not seem to come under the same heading as paralysis of limbs, and that facial paralysis is much less apparent and much rarer compared to spasms. This can be connected to what is seen in hypnosis as it is manifest in hysterics with stigmata; there facial spasms are easy to evoke by suggestion, whereas facial paralyses, at least in my experience, never appear very clearly.

Let's move on now to the other point that has to be underscored in our observations. We must in this patient, of whom we know so far only his current state, examine the illness's evolution, its antecedents, and particularly we must seek out the various etiological elements that came into play so as to evaluate them appropriately as far as possible and to note those that have exerted a dominant influence.

To begin with, this is a subject who has always been nervous. In his childhood he was difficult and liable to violent rages. No characteristic illnesses during this period. We shall speak later of his hereditary antecedents.

At sixteen he takes up the profession of cooper, and at nineteen he already had fully developed alcoholic habits. That, it seems, is inherent to the trade. He drank five or six liters of wine daily, an average of four small glasses of brandy, and occasionally, though rather rarely, a little absinthe, vermouth, and some vulnerary [used for treating wounds].

Although absinthe has often been accused of being the culprit, he asserted several times and apparently with great sincerity, after innocently confessing all possible excesses with wine and liquor, that he did not regularly drink absinthe, that he took it rarely, that he doesn't like it, and specifically that he never drank five or six glasses a day as we had been told. We find no good reason for not believing these often reiterated assertions, for on the whole we do not see that the abuse of wine and brandy could be less shameful to admit than excesses with absinthe or vermouth. On the contrary, for, if I'm not mistaken, absinthe, among those classes that abuse it, passes rather for an aristocratic drink. It's important to bring this out, because I think I can recognize our patient's story in an important publication, coming from a good source, where he is presented as an "absinthe addict." The nervous accidents we described above, namely: convulsive epileptoid attacks with the trunk thrust forward; hyperanesthetic sites on the left cheek where the pressure determines the production of circular convulsions, as are seen in ovarian hysterics—all these accidents are considered as derived directly from intoxication with absinthe and as contributing to the clinical picture. As far as I am concerned, and you will have understood this from what I have already said, I cannot see our patient as just a case of hysteria, "like any other," in which alcoholism—not absinthe—plays a major role etiologically as the precipitating agent, but in which trauma too, as we shall see, exerts an influence.

In 1885, at the age of eighteen, he is the victim of his first traumatic accident. But the time had not yet come, it seems, and he was able to stand a violent blow on the neck from a leaded cane that caused a wound which still leaves a scar, without any lasting nervous disturbance. He was cared for at the Pity Hospital, and in three weeks he had healed completely.

In 1887 a second accident: as an employee at a wine depot, he had been working one day in a cellar filling enormous barrels when suddenly a whole pile of these badly stacked hogsheads moves; an avalanche of barrels falls on him, threatening to pin him against a wall that cuts off his escape. It's then that he falls into an unspeakable nervous state about which he still can't talk today without emotion. His legs tremble beneath him and threaten to give way; instead of fleeing danger, he is incapable of moving and stays there as if transfixed. He hears his fellow workers call out to him in vain, telling him how to escape: he doesn't budge. Fortunately they take the initiative in helping him, dragging him out from there safely, without any wound or contusion, even fully conscious, but trembling all over. After a few hours he had completely recovered, and could resume work the same day.

It has to be pointed out that the effects of this nervous shock as a result of this accident didn't cease to be apparent for a period of three months. Every night during that time his sleep was disturbed by terrible nightmares in which he thought he was falling into a precipice or reliving the scene of the barrels rolling onto him.

Meanwhile, about two months after the accident, the first hysteroepileptic attack occurred. He was at the depot, doing his usual work when suddenly after experiencing the symptoms of the cephalic [vein] aura: whistlings in his ears, throbbing in his temples, vertigo, he falls unconscious. It seems that this first attack lasted about an hour. He had hit his chin on a barrel, and when he came round, blood was streaming from his mouth. In his fall on his chin he had pinched hard the internal surface of his lips between his teeth. His tongue had not been bitten.

Four months later he went into the army and the other soldiers, in making fun of him, made him notice "that when he laughs, his mouth is askew." That was the first notation of the facial paralysis that is still there today and that we are going to examine in detail.

The role of trauma is therefore easy to recognize: the great psychological agitation (nervous shock) of the accident with the barrels creates a permanent nervous state that results after several months in the first attack. In that attack, the fall onto his chin, in accordance with the laws that determine the localization of the phenomena of traumatic hysteria at the points hit and in their vicinity, leads to the appearance of the facial paralysis and the anesthesia that is superimposed on it. But the force of intoxication is not therefore diminished: it is clearly manifest in the following circumstances. The first attack had taken place, as I said, some months before he went into the army. In the army he is obliged to abstain for lack of money. From then on he no longer has major attacks, only little bouts of vertigo that sometimes hit him while on duty. As soon as he quits the army, that is to say, after a year, he goes back to his trade of cooper and at the same time to his habits of drinking, and then his convulsive attacks reappear with foam at the mouth, circular movements, etc., such as we observe today.

There is therefore here, as Dr. Guinon has cleverly put it in his important paper, "an accumulation of etiological factors," but in the total picture the trauma and the alcoholism cannot be taken as the precipitating factors; the true cause does not lie there; it's in the predisposition, in the nervous heredity which, by the way, is very pronounced in our patient. His father, a former soldier, employed at the tollhouse, was very nervous, very angry, and addicted to drink. His mother, irritable, exceedingly nervous, was subject to nervous attacks. During the last years of her life she had begun to drink; she was hospitalized at Saint-Anne [lunatic asylum] as insane. These are the facts; given our knowledge today of the sequence of causes in hysteria, they require no commentary.

Let's end with a few words about the therapy and prognosis. The influence of nervous heredity is there, always present, but one can nevertheless hope to attenuate its impact. Besides, even though adhering to the lesser role of chance causes, the practical importance of one of them can, however, not be ignored; I mean alcoholism, whose effect, daily reinforced by further abuse of the poison, supports the evil and aggravates its effects. At each new excess, it seems as if the fire were kindled again and we witness a new explosion of convulsive accidents temporarily dormant. On the other hand, we have seen that during his military service, when the patient couldn't drink for lack of money, he had had only vertigo and no major attacks. Consequently, the first thing to do is to preach abstinence. For some time now he has been conforming to our orders and drinks only milk; we have already been able to note the good effects of this treatment; the crises are much further apart. Hydrotherapy and tonics will do the rest, I hope. It would be sad if an intelligent and well endowed lad of twenty-four were to be condemned to lead an unhappy life from now on, having become incapable of courageously taking his place in society. I hope we will be able to make him fit to earn his living. But I fear that he will have to change trade. I think that he should not be exposed to relapse into the errors inherent, it seems, to the trade of cooper.

"A CASE OF RETRO-ANTEROGRADE AMNESIA PROBABLY OF HYSTERICAL ORIGIN"
REVUE DE MÉDECINE 12 (1892)

The clinical study to which we are going to devote today's lesson could be titled: *On a Case of Retro-Anterograde Amnesia Probably of Hysterical Nature and Origin*. Gentlemen, before presenting the patient who is to be the object of this study, I think it necessary to give some preliminary explanations.

The case concerns a woman of about thirty-four, who lives in C. . . , married to a decent man who is a joiner. Theirs is a family of modest people whose home is full of calm and tranquility. Surrounded by her husband and two children, she lived simply and peacefully as a good mother. Her life had always been happy until the day when an event upset her profoundly. It occurred on 28 August. About four o'clock in the afternoon, she was told point-blank of her husband's death; the news proved wrong, but the blow had been struck and when, several minutes later, the husband was brought back, she fell into a nervous state characterized above all by a delirium of which I will give you all the details in time.

For the time being, I will limit myself to this: when, on 31 August, this woman emerges from her delirium, she has lost the memory of all that has happened, to her knowledge, in the past six weeks, that is, since the evening of 14 July. However, she knows all the facts of what had happened before, from her earliest childhood up to 14 July, and she knows them perfectly; she can give an account of them with an exactness and precision that testify to her truly accurate and brilliant memory. But, I repeat, from the morning of 15 July, there is nothing more in her memory; it's a dark night. Nor is she aware of the event that is the cause of the affliction, I mean the news of her husband's death and the resulting three-day-long crisis.

This period of six weeks extending from 15 July to 28 August, let's call it, if you will, *the period of retrograde amnesia* (BC), to use a term already hallowed by usage and borrowed from the history of traumatic amnesias. We will reserve the name *normal period* for the period AB, which extends from her birth to 14 July, and which comprises more than thirty-three years, filled with innumerable events of which the patient has kept a perfect memory.

Now, what should be underlined in passing, during the lapse of time forgotten by the patient (the period of retrograde amnesia), her memory functioned *in an absolutely normal manner,* as is testified by the people around her and those who lived with her. Gentleman, her memory remained normal until 28 August. But the nefarious event and the mental dislocation following it had, in this respect, a retroactive effect. All those memories accumulated during six weeks were as if swept away; they no longer exist, or *seem no longer to exist.* I beg you to notice this reservation; you will shortly come to know the reason for it.

So now we are at 31 August, after the crisis that lasted for three whole days. It is then that this most extraordinary fact of the retrograde amnesia is noticed, an amnesia, as I've already told you, that extends over the six weeks prior to 28 August. It is then noticed that this amnesia also covers the period of the crisis itself (CD). Finally and especially it is noticed that from that same moment onward the patient has become *incapable thenceforth of registering* in her memory the *daily happenings whatever they may be.* Not only does she not know what has happened since 14 July; she is also incapable of remembering what she hears, what is happening around her; she can barely retain the memory of an impression from minute to minute and then everything disappears irrevocably whether the phenomena are visual, auditory, or motor. This is a general amnesia in the widest sense of the term.

So, gentlemen, this state has lasted for *four months* without any kind of change. This woman thus still has retrograde amnesia today, but also and above all permanent *current amnesia* since the event of 28

August. It is this last phenomenon to which I want particularly to draw
your attention. This current amnesia applies exclusively to the facts
that have accumulated since the event and that occur every day. In
regard to happenings before 15 July, today as on the day of the crisis
and as always since then, the organs of memory function perfectly,
even brilliantly, as I told you. A strange contrast that makes this case
exceptional, perhaps unique up to now!

Let's call, if you will, this period extending from 31 August to the
present the *period of anterograde amnesia* (DE), as against the retrograde period. You now understand the meaning of this designation
retro-anterograde amnesia that I proposed to you at the beginning of this
lesson. If I added: likely of hysterical nature and origin, it is because,
in my opinion—and that's the opinion I want to establish—the crisis,
the origin of the affliction, was an attack of major hysteria.

We have good reason to believe that this is not a matter of irreme-
diably destructive dynamic phenomena, but solely of transitory
organic disturbances. This opinion will be sufficiently corroborated if
we manage to demonstrate that hysteria is in play, for the manifestations of hysteria, though often tenacious, generally end in recovery. I
called it an anterograde not a progressive amnesia for things remain
in their original state. They are anterograde in relation to the time
that has passed since their appearance. But they have been, since the
beginning, what they are today: at one fell swoop they reached their
zenith. Apart from an abrupt start and a stable disposition from the
outset, which are generally not bad signs, there is, gentlemen, another
fact that is apt to make us hope for a favorable prognosis. You have
already noticed a certain reservation when I spoke to you of the very
marked character of our patient's amnesia. In telling you of the retrograde period, I said that the memories accumulated then no longer
exist *or appear* no longer to exist. In speaking of the anterograde and
the current period, I insisted on the fact that this woman *does not register* the happenings that occur. Her impressions, I told you, hardly last
a minute, then fade and cannot be retrieved. Well, those words, *she
does not register,* are too absolute. In reality, the events that she forgets
so quickly in her waking state and which she cannot retrieve into her
consciousness, she has in fact registered them. The proof of this is that
she has been able to recognize them spontaneously at night, in her
sleep. We have had her observed by her two neighbors in the adjacent
beds and so we have learned that she dreams out loud and that in her
dreams she sometimes alludes to the happenings of previous days,
thus evoking in her sleep memories that she is incapable of retrieving

in the waking state. But the proof lies above all in the following fact: this woman, whom we have been able to hypnotize, recovers in hypnotic sleep the memory of all the events that have occurred up to the present moment, and all the memories thus registered unconsciously are restored under hypnosis, systematically associated without a break so as to form a continuous thread like a second self, but a latent, unconscious self that contrasts strangely with the public self whose profound amnesia is known to you.

I therefore had grounds for hoping, gentlemen, that the situation is basically less serious than it at first appeared. We are not dealing here with a destructive amnesia, but with a purely dynamic one. If a jolt, a nervous shock, a change in the polarization of the organic elements of memory should intervene, then everything could revert to good order. And already you glimpse posthypnotic suggestion as the healing method; the conscious self will thus gradually assimilate the memories of the unconscious self, and conscious or psychological memory will recuperate all these apparently lost memories and thereby become richer. What is more, under the influence of this sort of methodical and frequently repeated exercise, the organs of memory will gradually relearn to function normally and to yield to the conscious self what it was reserving for the unconscious.

Do not feel excessive fright, gentlemen, at these studies, which move squarely into psychology. Don't forget that psychology belongs, to a certain degree, to the realm of medicine, and that it is, all in all, at least in its major aspect, nothing but the physiology of the higher or nobler areas of the brain.

It now remains for me to give proof of the propositions I have put forward. The task will perhaps be somewhat difficult, but with a little attentive patience on your part we shall succeed, I hope, in accomplishing it. Before bringing the patient in, I would like still to add a few words to give you some information that she likely could not hear without painful feelings. They refer to the family's antecedents. Mrs. D. . . , thirty-four years old, a seamstress, living in C. . . , came to Paris on 5 November, without being aware of it, to undergo preventive treatment for rabies. She underwent this treatment in its entirety and has no memory of it. On 10 November she came for the first time to the Salpêtrière, armed with a letter from Dr. J. . . (in C. . .) about the nervous illness afflicting her. After having been seen for about a fortnight, she was finally hospitalized in the Cruveilher ward, bed no. 17. Her mother, who was very emotional, had no real nervous attacks, but sometimes she fell to the ground in the wake of family discussions;

she died of an apoplectic stroke. Her father, it appears, was a violent man, a drunkard, debauched, who separated from his wife in unusual circumstances. This stain of debauchery and drunkenness we find to a very pronounced extent in nearly all the members of the family on the paternal side. Finally, Mrs. D. . .'s sister is a nervous woman who faints easily when anyone opposes her.

The time has come to present the patient to you. As you can see, she is a normal looking woman, in good health, with no anomaly other than that I have already outlined for you, I mean the defectiveness of her memory. I should tell you, however, that she has always been quite emotional and very anxious; she has always been afraid of spiders, dogs, rats—a trifle would frighten her: one day, a neighbor hidden behind her door frightened her so that she fainted in terror. But apart from this excessive emotionalism, we have not been able to find anything interesting in her past. After a childhood and a youth without pathological accident, she got married at twenty and had three children; after her marriage, as before, her health has always been perfect. But I must mention a series of little accidents that have happened in the last three years that the patient herself has told us about and that her husband and her doctor have confirmed. On one occasion she sustained an injury to her thigh, on another a wound on her hand. Later, a burn on her wrist, a rat bite; finally a madwoman hounded her for several months with anonymous letters and threats. Such is, in brief, the series of little mishaps that could perhaps have prepared a terrain already predisposed by heredity.

It's also from the patient herself that we have the information about the antecedents to the evening of 14 July. She has told us this with such an abundance of details that it would be impossible to pass it on to you in full. My assistant, Dr. Souques, who took the history with great care, will publish it separately. I will simply tell you that of all the events before 15 July, without exception, whether they are far from that date or near it, this woman's memory is uniformly felicitous. The event itself, the circumstances that preceded or followed it, the day, the date, sometimes even the time, everything is there with an accuracy of which we would for the most part be incapable. She knows very well the events of her childhood, the circumstances of her marriage, the exact day and date of her children's birth, etc. She also knows all the details about a wedding she attended on 6 July: in the morning the review of the children of the public school on square B. . . ; in the afternoon the inspection of the firefighters of C. . . with speeches by the mayor and the police chief; in the evening the fire-works, etc. She went to bed at about 10.30 p.m.

But after that moment her darkness is total. On the morning of 15 July *she must have,* she says, got up at about 6 a.m. as usual, but she knows absolutely nothing about this. Ask her what has happened since then, she will invariably reply: I don't know; I don't remember.

So now I will tell you what has happened since 15 July, based on the narrative of the patient's husband. First, in the retrograde period, nothing abnormal: no change in her state of health, no change in her character, no mental disturbance. You know, however, that all the memories accumulated in this period have disappeared completely. This disappearance occurred at one go following the tragic event of 28 August. Why does the break set in so utterly on the evening of 14 July? I will not be able to give you a satisfactory explanation. We know that this is the case in amnesias of traumatic origin so well documented by Azam, that the same retroactive effect is found, with similar limits, in amnesias following an attack of epilepsy or puerperal eclampsia. The same sudden break is also found in the amnesia that follows a violent moral emotion. Dr. Rouillard and Dr. Arnozan have each separately cited an example of this kind. Now, in our patient there was a violent emotion. Couldn't one conceive here of one of those rare cases of amnesia as a result of a moral shock? We shall see shortly what to make of this.

I told you, gentlemen, that this woman had forgotten *all* the events of the retrograde period. Some of them are, however, quite striking. On 17 August, she went to visit R. . . , which she had never seen, together with some of her friends; she came back full of wonder at the beauty of the sea, the park, the casino. Some days before, the prize giving at her daughter's school in C. . . had taken place. This prize giving, this trip to R. . . , which had made such a vivid impression on her, she has forgotten them completely. And this profound, absolute forgetting seems irremediable. But be assured, these memories are not irrevocable; you will shortly see them reappear in natural sleep and in induced sleep.

We have come at last to the event of 28 August. It was about four o'clock in the afternoon; our patient had just left a neighbor at whose house she usually worked; she had come home about a quarter of an hour earlier when suddenly a man crossed the threshold of her open door, and brusquely, without any ado, says to her: "Mrs. D. . . , get a bed ready; your husband is dead; he will be brought here." You can well guess this poor woman's emotion and grief. The neighbors come running in at her cries of despair and she tells them the scene I've just told you. Soon there's a crowd in the house and, while the customary consolation is being extended to this unhappy woman, a bystander runs for information, finds the husband in his workshop, and brings him back. A neighbor, seeing him from afar, has the bad idea of shouting: Here he is. At these words, thinking no doubt that her dead husband was about to be carried in, Mrs. D. . . falls into a nervous crisis that I must spell out to you in detail. On entering, the husband finds her unconscious, in an attack of suffocation, her hands held before her chest, around her neck, as if to disengage them. She was writhing, it seems, thrashing about to such an extent that her limbs and her head had to be held to avoid contusions. Her stays were unlaced and after she had been undressed she was put to bed. There, fifteen to twenty minutes after the beginning of this convulsive crisis, the agitation and the suffocation ceased, yielding without the least interval of lucidity, to delirium: "What a misfortune!" she said, "my poor children, you can weep. . . ." Her hands tear at her body . . . "Leave him to me still; I want to keep him. . . . Poor Jeanne, she has no mourning clothes." And this delirium lasted fourteen hours, fixated incessantly on these funereal scenes. Then this delirium with visual hallucinations is succeeded by a profound state of lethargy that lasts a day and from which no kind of stimulation can arouse her. Finally she seems to regain her senses, recognizes those around her, speaks to them and embraces them, but this return to reason was short-lived; ten minutes later the hallucinatory delirium recurs with a change in the picture: "Oh! This man . . . , this man . . . ," she shouted, raising herself in her bed in a posture of fright, as if to flee a terrifying vision. She is held down, calmed, spoken to; she replies, acknowledging the erroneousness of her senses, but almost immediately the delirium returns in the same manner. These hallucinations and this delirium persist for two days, punctuated by intervals of reason of varying length. Finally, on emerging from this attack of hysterical delirium, Mrs. D. . . found herself in the state in which you see her today.

I just said hysterical attack, for this is certainly a case of hysteria despite the absence of actual stigmata. The description that I have just given, drawing on the testimony of the doctor and of the witnesses, can leave no doubt in your minds.

I could, moreover, add in order to convince you fully, that under hypnosis the patient told us that the crisis had been preceded by ovarian pain on the right side, by the sense of a globus in her throat, a feeling of strangulation, beating in the temples, headache . . . , in short the classical sequence of the aura. So that now nothing is missing in the picture and the existence of a hysteroepileptic attack becomes indisputable.

This attack lasted for three whole days. So, gentlemen, we have come to the evening of 31 August: the crisis is over, the delirium has disappeared, and reason has returned. It is then, as I said, that this strange phenomenon of retrograde amnesia is noted by those around her. It is then that the even stranger phenomenon that I have called anterograde amnesia is discovered. People realize—I dwell on this fact—that she forgets in an instant what she has just done, said, heard, or seen. Things seen or heard before, she always thinks that she is seeing or hearing them for the first time. And this forgetfulness encompasses all the things that have happened in the course of the day. This amnesia has lasted right up to the present. All the things that have happened since that day she doesn't know. This is indeed a current, very singular amnesia for which it would be difficult to find an analogous example. I know that in traumatic amnesias certain facts of this kind have on rare occasions been noted and a sketch of the nature of anterograde amnesia can be found in the observations of Dr. Motet, Dr. Ribot, and Dr. Kaempfen. But the anterograde aspect is barely sketched there; it is moreover essentially ephemeral and not comparable either in degree or in duration to our case in which the amnesia has lasted for four months. That is the salient, central fact. A short questioning of the patient will give you a sample of her amnesia.

Q. - Do you know R. . . , madame?
A. - No, sir, I have never been there.
Q. - Has your daughter won any prizes this year?
A. - I don't know.
Q. - Do you remember whether in August a person wrongly told you of your husband's death?
A. - I have never heard anything of the sort.
Q. - What is that wound on your right hand?
A. - It's a burn.
Q. - When and how did you burn yourself?
A. - I don't know anything about it.
Q. - Isn't it a dog's bite?
A. - I've never been bitten by a dog.
Q. - Have you never been to Paris?
A. - No, sir.
Q. - You've never seen the Eiffel Tower, the Louvre?

A. - Never.

Q. - Do you know the Pasteur Institute?

A. - Yes, by name; I've never been there. It's in Paris.

Q. - Where are you?

A. - I don't know; I don't know this room.

Q. - Do you know the Salpêtrière?

A. - I've never seen it, but I've heard it mentioned.

Q. - Do you know these two women [her two neighbors in the beds next to hers]?

A. - No, sir, I've never seen them.

Q. - And this gentleman (Dr. S., the assistant)?

A. - Not at all.

Q. - And me, do you know me?

A. - (After a short reflection) . . . *Yes, you are Dr. Charcot.* . . . Am I then in Paris?

Q. - Have you had breakfast this morning?

A. - I don't know; I must have had breakfast because I'm not hungry.

Q. - Who brought you here just now? Where do you come from?

A. - I don't know.

Q. - What day is it?

A. - Oh, sir, I don't know the day nor the month; I don't know how I live; I'm very unhappy.

Q. - What did I just ask you?

A. - I've already forgotten; I no longer know . . . ; it's no use looking; I can't find it.

I think it's futile, gentlemen, to continue this questioning in your presence. You see the complete contrast, the absolute break between the accuracy of her memory of things before 14 July and the defectiveness of her memory for facts after this date. You see that she doesn't know any of the events since 14 July, that she doesn't know where she is, what she has done this morning, what she has just said and done, and that she forgets almost instantly current facts. This memory loss is as profound as it is total, however intense and repeated her impressions may have been. So she doesn't recognize Dr. S., my assistant, who has been questioning her daily for a month; she doesn't recognize her two neighbors in the next beds with whom she lives from morning to night. There is, however, an exception, one only: she recognized me and found my name. Because, gentlemen, she has known me by name for a long time already; she has even known me in effigy for several years, consequently for a period before last 14 July she has seen my portrait in the office of her doctor in C. . . , on the picture by Brouilhet of *A Lesson at the Salpêtrière,* and she has seen it often.

When I arrived in the ward, we showed her a copy of this picture, which she immediately found like her doctor's engraving; she looked at me, grasped the resemblance, and said: *You are Dr. Charcot.* We have several times obliged her to make this comparison and this recognition. Later, when I asked her whether she recognized me, she spontaneously looked at the picture and pronounced my name. But my presence is necessary for this recall, for she asserts that has never seen me if she is questioned on this subject in my absence.

In reality, in her current amnesiac state she knows my name and my portrait as acquisitions from the past, and these old memories allow her by a process of comparison and reasoning to recognize me when she sees me so that this memory is no exception to the current amnesia. The recognition stems primarily from notions gleaned from the past. Nevertheless, there is in it something acquired. When I ask her who I am, she directly turns her eyes to the wall as if she knew that a particular picture hangs precisely in that spot. There is, it seems to me, in that movement a sort of unconscious acquisition, but it's the only one we have been able to note so far.

Despite the current amnesia that is so rapid and so pronounced, Mrs. D. . . has attended very properly, it appears, to caring for her household and to seeing to the normal necessities of life. After the delirious crisis, she quickly noticed her amnesia—she must still be perfectly aware of it today—and the inconveniences of this condition. She then had the idea of resorting to the use of a notebook to supplement her defective memory. In this notebook she wrote, for she can write, read, and calculate perfectly, what she had to do, what she had done, her shopping, her expenses, her errands, etc. Thanks to this method, thanks above all to her neighbors' and her children's help, she has been able to manage to run her household. She put this notebook in her pocket (she has only one), where she would inevitably find it. Through this habit she has gradually acquired the unconscious idea that she has a memorandum book, for very often while being questioned, she spontaneously puts her hand in her pocket, takes the notebook out of it, and opens it in order to read the answer if it happens to be there. This memory is in reality an unconscious memory, for she doesn't know this notebook's size, shape, or color; she recognizes it only after opening it and recognizing in it her own handwriting. And here, too, in the acquisition of this memory, reasoning seems to have played an important part.

Gentlemen, this amnesia in the anterograde period affects not only ordinary life happenings but also memorable events. Isn't the event of last 30 October a memorable one? In a village street our amnesiac was bitten by a dog suspected of having rabies; she immediately records the fact in her notebook. The wound is cauterized twice, and the decision is immediately made to send her to Paris. But she has forgotten this event; she therefore arrives in Paris after a long journey without knowing it and undergoes rabies treatment for fifteen days. Without knowing it, she stays in Odeon street with old friends, whom she has known for twenty years; she went sightseeing to the major Parisian monuments and shops without knowing it. Without knowing it, she was finally on 23 November admitted to the Salpêtrière, where she is now, without knowing it. The arrangement of the beds lets her recognize a hospital, but she is incapable of saying whether this is a hospital in Paris or in Bordeaux. She knows only that it isn't the hospital in C. . . , which she has known since her childhood, and so manages to deduce logically that she cannot be, that she isn't in C. . . .

Since this woman has been on the ward, despite the high degree of her amnesia, we have become convinced that the defect in her memory is purely apparent. I will explain what I mean. As you know, we have learned from her neighbors that she would dream aloud, that in her dreams she would sometimes speak of this or that event during the amnesiac period, either the retrograde or the anterograde one, that she would say for example: "Dr. Charcot . . . I don't want any showers. . . . That wretched dog bit me and tore my dress." These dreams, uttered aloud, would already testify strongly to the unconscious deposit in her memory of events she doesn't know in her waking state. Later attempts at hypnotism, crowned with success, have come to confirm the existence of this deposit and to show in a peremptory and indisputable manner the storing of all the things that have happened since the evening of 14 July up to the present. In hypnotic sleep she has told us all the events of this period, apprising us even of details we didn't know and whose authenticity we have since been able to check. She told us the scene of 28 August, the dog bite, the arrival in Paris, the antirabies treatment, her sightseeing in Paris, her admission to the Salpêtrière, etc., with a very striking facility and accuracy that we will let you judge for yourselves.

But while we set about putting her to sleep, we must, gentlemen, discuss the nature of this strange amnesia. I shall limit myself here exclusively to the medical aspect, leaving the psychological aspect aside by choice. Quite evidently, it is not an organic lesion, a grave lesion resulting, for instance, from a softening of the brain. It is hysteria, gentlemen, that is at play here, solely hysteria. Now, the convulsive, delirious attack lasted three days. Couldn't one, in order to explain this hysteria, invoke a profound disturbance, a nervous exhaustion following this long crisis? I don't think so. In my opinion, it is simply the equivalent of a prolonged hystero-epileptic attack in the shape of amnesia. You know that the delirious period of an attack is often transformed, and that this transformation can assume very different clinical forms. You know that hysterical somnambulism, perhaps also spontaneous somnambulism, is nothing other than a transformation of this delirious phase of the attack, and that ambulatory automatism and hysterical sleep stem, in theory, from the same interpretation. So, in our patient, there is a transformation of the delirious phase of the classical attack, but a transformation into an amnesiac mode, a highly original mode, hitherto unknown, if I'm not mistaken. And the lengthy duration of this amnesia will not astonish you if you think of the often very prolonged duration of some attacks of hysterical sleep.

Now, gentlemen, we will together question this woman in her hypnotic sleep.

Q. - Madam, do you know R. . . ?

A. - Yes, sir. I was there on 17 August with Mr. and Mrs. V. We saw the park, the Casino; I saw a woman playing a game and she lost 500 francs. In the evening we went to the theater and we didn't get back to C. . . until the next day by the midday train.

Q. - Did your daughter win any prizes this year?

A. - She won three: for reading, writing, and spelling, in which she came first, I think.

Q. - What happened at your house on 28 August?

A. - I had just left Mrs. V.; I was in the midst of sewing an apron on the machine when a man I didn't know comes and says abruptly: "Your husband is dead; he is to be brought here; get a bed ready, Mrs. D. . ." He must have known my name. I was so shocked that I suddenly collapsed; my head hit the needle holder on the machine and made a small wound that hurt me for several days. I then felt that man touch my shoulder and say: "Instead of being so upset, go on upstairs and get a bed ready." Then he left, I don't know how, I was so overwhelmed.

Q. - And the business about the dog?

A. - It was on 30 October, a Friday, at 9 a.m. I was on the road to S. . . ; I was looking for lodgings, a little yellow dog bit my hand and tore my dress. A woman came to help me and told me I must have it cauterized, because there were some dogs with rabies in the town. I wrote that in my notebook. I was burned with alkali, then with a cautery iron.

Q. - When did you come to Paris?

A. - I came to Paris on 5 November with my husband; we stayed with Mr. L. . . in Odoen street. Every day for fifteen days we went for inoculations at the Pasteur Institute, etc.

Q. - Who are those women?

A. - They are the neighbors to my bed; they came with me to the reception room a little while ago. They are in beds 16 and 18 in the Cruveilher ward. They are Mrs. C. and Mrs. X. . .

Q. - What is the date, madame?

A. - Tuesday, 22 December.

I think it superfluous, gentlemen, to continue this dialogue. You see that the apparently forgotten memories are inscribed in her unconscious persona. Her hypnotic sleep is really filled with facts registered in the sleeping state. The contrast is striking, and my initial reservation entirely justified. Since this is the case, you will say, nothing is easier than to benefit from hypnotic sleep in order to make suggestions to the patient and so to restore her memory. That is indeed the procedure we propose to carry out as these posthypnotic suggestions have already produced some results. Couldn't one consider provoking a hysterical crisis in hopes of seeing this attack undo what the other had done? This could be tried, I believe, and with all the more likelihood of success as the modifications in the delirious phase of the attack are usually circumscribed between the two hysterical attacks. However, since our patient presents no hysterogenic area, we prefer for the time being to stick to hypnotic suggestion, plus the usual other helpful aids: hydrotherapy, tonics, etc. Unfortunately we have to fear that it may take a long time before we achieve completely satisfactory results.

I have finished, gentlemen. I did not want to discuss the truly absurd hypothesis of fraud and pretense. I could in that context have raised an interesting problem in legal medicine, but I prefer to leave you with the impression of a curious pathological fact, simple and perhaps unique of its kind.

5

Pierre Janet

JANET WAS A NEAR CONTEMPORARY OF FREUD, BORN JUST FIVE YEARS before him (1859) and outliving him by six years, dying in 1947. The earlier part of his career was also overshadowed by the august presence of Charcot, whose pupil he was. As a result partly of his historical situation and partly of his unassuming manner Janet has tended to be rather overlooked, certainly in comparison to Charcot and Freud. Yet his contribution to the shaping of the case history and to the treatment of nervous illnesses was quite momentous.

Janet's formation and career path were somewhat unconventional. He began as a student of philosophy, taking his *agrégation*, roughly the equivalent of the master's degree, in 1882. From 1883 onward he taught philosophy in high school, first briefly in the rural area of Châteauroux in central France, and then from 1883 to 1889 in the much larger maritime, industrial, and commercial town of Le Havre. While there he witnessed some of the then fashionable spectacular stage performances of hypnotism. Perhaps it was these demonstrations that aroused his interest in hysteria, for during his stays in Paris he began to accompany his brother, Jules, a medical student, on his visits to patients. Janet also began to do voluntary work at the hospital in Le Havre as well as psychiatric research. Psychiatry was then still loosely allied to philosophy as a theoretical, speculative field, not yet fully integrated into scientific medicine. Janet considered writing his doctoral thesis on hallucinations but could not find enough suitable subjects in the small ward at the hospital in Le Havre. For his doctorate in philosophy in 1889 he wrote *Automatisme psychologique* (Psychological Automatism), which was to remain a lifelong interest of his.

In November 1889 he embarked on the study of medicine in Paris; from 1890 onward he spent much time on Charcot's wards at La Salpêtrière, and Charcot chaired the committee at the defense of his thesis in medicine in July 1893. After qualifying as a physician, Janet went on working with relative freedom at La Salpêtrière, continuing to do so after Charcot's sudden death in 1893. His main field was experimental psychology, which he also taught at the Sorbonne (1893–99). He regarded himself less as a doctor of nervous diseases than as an experimental psychologist whose primary interest was shifting from hysteria to neurasthenia. In July 1892 he presented a paper on the relation of amnesia to unconscious fixed ideas at the International Congress of Experimental Psychology, a case that clearly anticipates the case history included here, originally published two years later. Throughout the early 1890s Janet published in the *Revue philosophique* a remarkable series of case histories, culminating in "The History of a Fixed Idea," often known simply as "Justine." As are Freud's "Dora," "The Wolfman," and "The Ratman," Janet's cases are frequently called after the name of their central figure (Léonie, Marcelle, Lucie) rather than by their full, at times cumbersome, academic titles. In 1893 he published his doctoral dissertation in medicine, *L'État mental des hystériques* (*The Mental State of Hysterics*, trans. R. C. Carson [New York: Putnam & Sons, 1901]).

Janet is reputed in the course of his long life to have recorded some five thousand case histories, which were stored in a dedicated room in his home, but he ordered that they be burned on his death so that only a handful have survived. These are cases published early in his career: the most substantial of these extant case histories appeared in the *Revue philosophique* between 1887 and 1894 (see bibliography). Among them is the "Histoire d'une idée fixe" (History of a Fixed Idea), the case chosen here, which is the last and, incidentally, the shortest one of the group in the *Revue philosophique*. None of these cases has ever been reprinted in French or translated so that these important early studies are hard to access. Among English-speaking audiences Janet is best known for the lectures he gave at Harvard later in his life, *Major Symptoms of Hysteria* (1920), a revised version of his 1893 doctoral dissertation.

The most immediately striking feature of "History of a Fixed Idea" is its inordinate length, compared to the case histories customary at the time; it is almost three times as long as Charcot's longest one. This expansiveness was all the more exceptional in contrast to the dominant and common habit of chronicling a cluster of cases with the aim of ascertaining and illustrating the specific characteristics of a particular syndrome. The method of rapidly surveying a group of cases was obviously the most appropriate one so long as the goal was to classify, as Krafft-Ebing does in his overview of sexual aberrations, or to establish a typology, as Schnitzler does in his six cases of functional aphonia. Charcot, too, saw his patients as variations on a category, namely, hysteria. Janet breaks away from this usage by opting in each of his early cases to devote his attention intensively to a single individual. The transition from the series to the individual becomes manifest, too, slightly later in Freud's switch from *Studien über Hysterie* (*Studies on Hysteria,* 1896), where a sequence of four patients (and some subsidiary parallel ones) is presented, to *Bruchstück einer Hysterie-Analyse* (*Fragment of an Analysis of a Case of Hysteria* [1905]), *Bemerkungen zu einem Fall von Zwangsneurose* (*Notes upon a Case of Obsessional Neurosis* [1909]), and *Aus der Geschichte einer infantilen Neurose* (*From the History of an Infantile Neurosis* [1918]), each of which deals at length with a singular individual. It is a reflection of this focus on the one figure that these cases, like Janet's, are popularly known simply by the name of the patient: Dora, the Ratman, and the Wolfman.

In devoting himself intensively to Justine in "History of a Fixed Idea," Janet was thus an innovator. He writes repeatedly of "studying" Justine with whose problems he becomes fascinated. He meets her when her husband takes her to the outpatient clinic at La Sâlpetrière in October 1890; by then, at age forty she had already exhibited increasingly bizarre symptoms for about twenty years. So as to study her thoroughly Janet sees her at least once a week, more frequently in phases of crisis, over a period of three years. The very title of this case history, "History of a Fixed Idea," projects a temporal depth and a developmental approach uncommon before Freud. Toward the end, as she improves, Janet deliberately tapers off the meetings in order to reduce her dependence on him, but he recognizes her continuing need for support, to "confess," as he puts it in quasi-theological terms, for if their meetings fall below once a month, she relapses. Invoking an educational rather than a medical analogy, Janet describes himself as Justine's "tutor." His phraseology as well as his method anticipate the behavioral modification approach of one type of modern psychotherapy. Janet's understanding that Justine is not permanently "cured," only improved, an improvement dependent on his readiness to go on seeing her at regular intervals (as if for periodic booster shots of encouragement), testifies to the strength of what would nowadays be termed the therapeutic alliance. The importance of such a supportive relationaship is confirmed when Janet cites a patient who has to be committed to hospital again after the death of her therapist.

Because of its considerable length Janet divides his account of Justine into five sections: "The Idea of Cholera," "The Secondary Fixed

Ideas," "Suggestibility and Abulia," "Education of the Mind," and
"Evolution of the Illness: Personal and Hereditary Antecedents." The
sections are complementary, each uncovering a further aspect of Justine's character and affliction. She is first introduced as in the grip of
a fixed idea, the fear of cholera; then various other facets of her illness are revealed. Each section is linear in its chronological progres-
sion; however, in totality the arrangement is, as it were, kaleidoscopic
so that cumulatively an increasingly complex profile of the patient
emerges. The sequence of the sections is in part regressive insofar as
the opening one deals with Justine's most immediate, that is, presenting complaint, while the last one has moved all the way back to
her antecedents. So this case history proceeds from the history of one
fixed idea to the history of ancillary fixed ideas, to the history of other
abnormal traits, and finally to the history ("evolution" in the sense of
unfolding) of the entire pathology. This structure serves to build up,
piece by piece, a complete, rounded image of Justine. The surprising
new vistas opened up in successive sections, as in a story by install-
ments (as, of course, in Freud's case histories as he delves into his
patients' past), heighten readers' interest as the perplexities grow by
accretion. The narrative organization is therefore more sophisticated
than it may appear to be; its directness of manner derives from the
scientific factuality as Janet reports on Justine with the maximal doc-
umentation he can marshal, yet at the same time it encompasses a literary element in the artfulness of its overall patterning.

It is not only in its length and articulation that the "History of a
Fixed Idea" differs from Charcot's and other previous case histories.
An even more crucial divergence resides in the quantity and nature
of the information Janet offers about his patient as well as in his relationship with her. From the outset the patient is individualized by
being dignified with a name instead of the then normative initial(s).
Janet provides far more than the customary cursory data on age, marital status, occupation, and family health history; he gives a rich picture of the events and circumstances of Justine's life, dense with
vivid detail from her childhood onward. He does so because of his
vital conviction that it is essential to understand the patient before
attempting to explain the illness. The importance of this insight can
hardly be overstated; here again Janet foreshadows Freud. Janet con-
ceives the illness as an intrinsic product of the patient's entire life,
not some extraneous entity that has intruded on it. He therefore
takes a developmental approach in his efforts to achieve an understanding of Justine. She comes across not as a mere object of study;

she is, much rather, a quirky, moody individual, constantly astonishing in the unexpected twists and turns of her life story. She imagines herself pregnant, she attacks her husband with a knife and wants to divorce him despite his kindness to her, she learns to play the piano and to do accounts, and so forth. As Janet watches and tries to guide her, he remains alert to her own utterances, often citing them, even if they seem alienating.

Through the persistence of his work with Justine, Janet establishes a distinctive relationship with her; when he refers to her as "notre malade" (our patient), he sounds almost affectionate. Admittedly, the French habit of using the magisterial first person plural in serious discourse has to be taken into account; yet the phrase also suggests a personal connection that extends metonymically by association to us as readers. Justine becomes more than a vessel of fixed ideas and eccentricities of all kinds; together with Janet, we encounter her as a strange human being in whom we grow as interested as Janet himself does. He is the spectator of her drama, the bystander who intervenes whenever he deems it necessary. Although he is the decisive agent of Justine's therapy, he remains largely the unobtrusive and sometimes amazed witness. Even as he guides Justine, he manages to do so tactfully, allowing her in the later stages to grow at her own volition and pace without dominating her. In short, Janet respects Justine's individuality, however bizarre her behavior. His posture toward his patient is in sharp contrast to that of Charcot, who always occupies the center of the stage and who is condescending to his patient, at times to the verge of being contemptuous.

Janet's restraint, his assumption of a low-key role for himself, and his abdication of omniscience underscore Justine's position as a mystery to her doctor and consequently to readers. As Charcot's case histories do, this one takes the form of a detective story in which the physician is the sleuth. Janet aims to probe the enigma that Justine represents, but as further puzzles emerge after the initial fixed idea is dispelled, the problem is never fully resolved, for unlike Charcot, who knows a priori that hysteria is the cause of his patients' disorders, Janet has no such ready answer. He never actually pins a diagnostic label onto Justine, although he mentions hysteria, a term he regards with some distrust as too undifferentiated. However, her susceptibility to hypnotism (somnambulism, as he calls it) and her very high degree of suggestibility seem to Janet, as to Charcot, indicative of hysteria. Justine is an incessant chameleon, who continues to pose ever new challenges to Janet. Even as she is tantalizing, she also represents an endless challenge to him because he is essentially an experimental psychologist with a strong impulse to fathom the mystery.

Experimentation entails for Janet tentativeness as he proceeds cautiously step by step. So this case history records more a process than a result; the result of Justine's improvement is almost a by-product of Janet's empirical experimentation, although as a physician he also clearly wants to remediate the patient. But it is not unfair to claim that while remediation must be his ultimate goal, the experiment itself draws his equal if not greater attention. At several points Janet elaborates in considerable detail on previously carried out experiments in psychology, notably in the area of visual perception and in so-called crystal-gazing.

This situation is by no means to the patient's disadvantage since ingenuity animates all experimentation. While Janet makes constant use of hypnotism to induce the state of altered consciousness he refers to as somnambulism, he also proves himself to be extraordinarily inventive in the strategies he devises to rid Justine of her fixed idea(s). For instance, his verbal games with the progressive conversion of the term *cholera* into something ultimately innocuous to Justine's mind is a brilliant ploy on his part. Similarly, his transformation of the corpses of the cholera victims by first clothing them and then turning them into a comical figure is as amusing as it is creative. Janet's modesty makes him quite apologetic about the unorthodox means he devises, saying that they may appear "childish" or "banal," yet they prove remarkably effective. The thrust of Janet's therapy is practical; he is willing to resort to whatever works with Justine. Instead of simply applying the standard medical treatments, he endeavors to find what best suits this particular patient. He appropriates hypnosis because it is the most effective way for him to influence Justine. But at the same time he hits on the tactic of training, a reeducation that goes beyond mere distraction as a long-range mode of behavior and thought modification that foreshadows current behavioral therapy.

Janet's creativity is also borne out by the paucity of his scholarly footnotes compared to those of Charcot and Schnitzler, who site their work in relation to that of their predecessors. Janet does refer to Breuer and Freud, but mainly he invokes those of his own previous cases that offer parallels to Justine. This reduction in the weight of the academic intertext places a greater emphasis on the expedient (in the positive sense) and, incidentally, makes this case history so eminently readable.

In keeping with his practicality Janet's main method for his experimentation is close, sustained observation of his patient. He uses what he calls the "fountain-pen method" to note all he sees and hears, and from his perceptions he tries to infer the significance of Justine's conduct. His modus operandi is, therefore, deductive, and, as far as possible, logical. Janet's pragmatism leads him to eschew precisely the kinds of large theoretical statements his peers favored. He opens the "History of a Fixed Idea" with a categoric rejection of "hasty generalizations" on the grounds that they result only in "narrow and absolute conceptions." This suspicion of generalizations underlies his highly important insistence right at the outset on the necessity "to try first of all to understand the patient before attempting to explain the illness." So in Janet's account of Justine direct observation and circumstantial detail always take precedence over "generalizations" even if they are far from "hasty" but the product of lengthy, meticulous attention to the patient. In the closing paragraph, as if to round off his report, Janet returns to the futility of putting forward "general comments" that could "hardly be justified by the study of a single patient." Janet's scrupulous focus in all his case histories on particular individuals, though it produces most interesting portraits and findings, nevertheless inevitably results in an at least seeming limitation of his horizon. His avoidance of generalizations has likely contributed to the relative neglect he has suffered in comparison to those who can readily be associated with a widely applicable concept such as Charcot's theories on hysteria. Janet paid a price for heeding individuals. The unique dual capacity simultaneously to gain insight into individuals *and* to formulate overarching ideas was one of Freud's outstanding qualities.

Through his focus on the individual Janet attains a far subtler appreciation of the key role of the unconscious. In his treatment of Justine's phobia of cholera, he quickly realizes that this fixed idea has origins far beyond the immediate fear of this disease and death. He works retrospectively to ferret out its more recondite sources. This probing takes him back to the impressions made on Justine in her childhood and adolescence of the moribund and dead patients cared for by her mother, who was a nurse. The idea of cholera has to be rendered harmless through transformation if it is to be successfully dislodged, as indeed it is. But the obsession with cholera proves to be merely the tip of a sizable iceberg as Janet discovers that Justine feels threatened by numerous "secondary" fixed ideas which he describes as stemming from *"derivation," "association,"* or *"suggestibility."* These sec-

ondary fixed ideas are of varying gravity and intensity, ranging from
the mildly comical to the fundamentally disruptive. Although they
surface as separate manifestations, Janet sees them as connected in
one way or another through their ulterior roots in the structure
of Justine's personality. So he understands the existence and effects
of "the deep layers of consciousness" implicated in the causation of
"deeper mental disturbances." His awareness of the role of the unconscious takes him to the exploration of dreams and to the use of
automatic writing, together with hypnosis, as paths of access to the
mind's underlying strata. While recognition of the unconscious was
certainly not new by the end of the nineteenth century (early in the
century the German romantics had been fascinated by what they
called the night side of existence, and Charcot saw the discrepancy
between the unconscious and the conscious self in the woman with
amnesia), Janet was the first forcefully to underscore its salient function in the shaping of behavior.

If Janet is in the avant-garde in his appreciation of the unconscious,
in some other respects he is a child of his age. His concern with the
possible physical underpinnings of Justine's fixed idea is characteristic of the priority given to the somatic at that time. He considers the
infectious diseases Justine had had early in her life, implying but not
actually stating the impact they might have exerted on her psychological development. It is easy enough to see how they might have
been implicated in the formation of her primary fixed idea of cholera
by fostering a preoccupation with death that surfaces as a well
defined phobia in the context of her mother's work. Later in Justine's
life, Janet notes that the aggravation of her symptoms coincided with
the onset of menstruation and was repeated every month at the time
of her period. As in other areas, so in weighing the interaction of the
physical with the psychological, Janet paints a complex picture that
cautiously balances the diverse factors without dogmatic pronounce-
ments. He respects the role of the somatic while bestowing priority
on the psychological, and he does so with a grain of humor all too
rare in case histories when he concedes that readers may "smile" at
his observation that Justine's hair became less dry and her weight
dropped astonishingly as her mental status improved.

Only in his endorsement of heredity is Janet wholly in conformity
with the accepted precepts of his time. The closing section, "Evolution of an Illness: Personal and Hereditary Antecedents," delves into
Justine's physical and psychological background, reaching back sev-

eral generations and comprising twenty-six relatives, not counting those infants who had died at an early age. Janet draws up a family tree, beginning with Justine's grandparents and tracing three generations descended from her parents, who had nine children, of whom five survived into adulthood. Justine is sited in a gallery of abominations: alcoholism, epilepsy, and imbecility abound, and there are also ample violence, cruelty, hysteria, brutality, jealousy, and viciousness. One of Justine's sisters, K., is described as being like her, obsessive. Since Justine herself has no children, she is a dead end in this proliferating clan.

The question marks on the family tree, especially in the earliest and the later generations, attest to the extent of Janet's uncertainty at several points. Because of the high incidence of imbecility or at least of low intelligence, Janet must have faced great difficulties in compiling this information. His essential honesty is very apparent as he openly admits the gaps in, as well as the dubiousness surrounding, some of the facts. Nonetheless, it is surely significant that despite these obstacles he investigates the issue of Justine's heredity in this expansive, exhaustive form. Arguably, this section on Justine's heredity can be seen as an extension of the examination of her social context. However, Janet is convinced that "this whole long illness" cannot be attributed solely to the "simple little accident" of going with her mother to bury the corpses of those who had died of cholera. Whether this was indeed a "simple little accident" for an obviously impressionable young woman is open to question; however, early encounters with death must have been much more common then than nowadays. What is important is Janet's argument that there must be an ulterior cause to trigger Justine's entire "transformation." It is in search of this ulterior cause that he turns to his patient's heredity, asserting that "in order to understand a thing well, an attempt must be made to go back to its origins." Janet was far too astute and cautious to ascribe Justine's illness unequivocally to one factor or another. It is characteristic of his thoroughness to pursue all the various possibilities. While eschewing definitive findings, he seems to settle on a confluence of immediate environmental experiences in Justine's life with the pervasive undertow of heredity as the roots of her illness. Again, with his characteristic modesty, he refuses to claim a cure despite the astonishing progress his patient makes under his care.

Janet writes in a direct, straightforward manner without the oratorical showmanship that Charcot favored. The abundance of his rhetorical questions springs from genuine uncertainty, whereas with Charcot they are an expression of his grandstanding, introduced for effect. Charcot possesses the answers; Janet is seeking them. His frequent recourse to the present tense not only gives immediacy to his account but also makes readers feel as though they are actually witnessing the scene. His occasional imagery further enhances the vividness of his report: the fixed ideas that invade and consume Justine are likened to parasites, and her suggestibility is compared to the labile state of an organism that had overcome an infection but remained weakened by it. Here again Janet is aligning psychological responses with the body's somatic reactions.

Janet's "History of a Fixed Idea" is remarkable above all for its serious, respectful, long-term engagement with a single patient. In this exclusive concentration on one case, it marks a significant departure from the established practice of seeking out the typology implicit in a series of similar cases. For Janet, generalization, of which he is so suspicious, and that was the objective and often the starting point for his immediate predecessors, takes a back seat to the understanding of a singular individual. This holds true for all the case histories he published in the *Revue philosophique* between 1888 and 1894. They represent an important turning point in the evolution of the genre. Clearly, they pave the way for Freud's case histories by prefiguring the focus on one particular person as the core of the narrative. However, where Freud goes beyond Janet is in his ability to open up the particular into the universal by imaginative reflection.

Janet is a very important transitional figure in the evolution of the case history and the handling of patients with nervous illnesses. Overshadowed for too long by the two giants flanking him, Charcot and Freud, he warrants far greater attention. His approach shows continuity from Charcot in the persistence of the diagnosis of hysteria (albeit with reservations and refinements), the use of hypnosis, and the belief in both the hysteric's special susceptibility to hypnosis and the power of heredity. But Janet departs from Charcot in his intense preoccupation with individual cases, in the consequent formation of an active therapeutic alliance that includes respect for the patient, and in his strong conviction of the force of the unconscious. In all these respects, he is clearly a forerunner of Freud. In psychoanalysis the subconscious assumed an absolutely central role and was invested with a previously inconceivable sexual potency that extended to all areas of human existence and relationships.

HISTORY OF A FIXED IDEA
REVUE PHILOSOPHIQUE 37:1 (1894): 121–68

It is difficult nowadays to formulate the psychological laws that determine mental illnesses: hasty generalizations always lead only to narrow and absolute conceptions. In this type of study, as in others, it is essential to stick to long observation and description of particular facts; it is good to try first of all to understand the patient before attempting to explain the illness. For this reason we will be excused if, in our research on fixed ideas, we will not yet go into the study nor the bibliography of the issue in a general way if we dwell instead on the analysis of a particular case. This will be an opportunity to verify the ideas we have already expressed in regard to another patient, and perhaps to point out some new ones.

The person to whom we devote today's study is a woman of forty, whom we will call Justine. We met her for the first time three years ago through Dr. Seglas, who was willing to entrust her to us. Without admitting her to hospital, which was not necessary, we got her to come and see us regularly in the different departments where we were doing our clinical studies. That is how we studied her at first every week, then at less frequent intervals for three years. Her mental state, which was very grave at the beginning, has happily gradually modified, and for over a year she has been well, at least as far as possible. This improvement now seems sufficiently stable to permit us to describe the patient's current state and to consider the study of this person as pretty complete for the time being.

When Justine was brought to the Salpêtrière by her husband in October 1890, she presented as follows. She is a tall, strong woman with thick, very black hair, very dark eyes, wide open and haggard; her regular features would not be displeasing if they were not disrupted by continual grimaces and tics; her face is alternately very pale, then veined with red blotches; her hands are moist and trembling, her gait unsteady. As soon as one tries to examine this woman, she hides her face in her hands and breaks into sobs: "Oh! It's terrible to live like this, I'm afraid, I'm afraid!—Of what?—I'm afraid of cholera." This word sums up the entire observation: this is a patient obsessed by a most banal fixed idea. Precisely because this idea is relatively simple, it struck us as useful to analyze it, to follow its evolution and, if possible, its disappearance. Although Justine's personal and hereditary antecedents are, in our opinion, highly interesting, we will not disclose them at the beginning of this study. To go into them would raise delicate questions that would distract us from our main subject, the analysis of a fixed idea. We will come back to them later when we will try to understand the nature and the origin of this malady.

I.—The Idea of Cholera

Without at present going into the various accidents that have characterized our patient's life, we will briefly review the facts relevant to the current fixed idea. Justine, who had always been extremely emotional, has since her youth been very frightened by the thought of death. This preoccupation with death was certainly heightened by her mother's profession. She was a nurse, and she often had to look after and to bury the dead; sometimes she even made her daughter help her in these distressing tasks. The sight of two corpses dead of cholera made a deep impression on Justine at age seventeen. When she went home, she was preoccupied, and although she did not complain of anything, she could not help thinking very frequently of these victims of cholera in the following years. This thought was not continuous; it would come back only in phases of sadness and fatigue, and still remained vague and imprecise; "it was merely an *idea*," said the patient in language that we will presently understand better. However, this young girl thought of death, dreamed of it even in her waking state; she felt an inner voice saying to her: "Give me your soul . . ." and she was surprised at her reply, uttered aloud: "No, no." The idea was already beginning to assume a pathological form.

The following year a mild attack of typhoid fever together with a laborious and insalubrious job in a tobacco factory led to a considerable aggravation of her morbid preoccupations. Several times a day Justine turned pale, broke out in cold sweats and trembling that could not be explained and that were due to the increasingly powerful thought of cholera. Her symptoms kept on getting worse and at about twenty-three we see the appearance of violent nervous attacks whose nature we will soon be able to assess. In accordance with popular opinion, it was hoped that these nervous accidents would be stopped by marriage; at twenty-eight Justine married a fine workman who has always been very devoted to his wife as well as indulgent. The marriage at first lessened the patient's lugubrious ideas by spawning two other diversionary fixed ideas. Justine thought she was pregnant and for several months showed all the signs of pregnancy. Finally she had to be convinced that this was not true, and she developed another fixed idea, a hatred of her husband and the thought of divorce. She went to lawyers to get out of her marriage and engaged in other eccentric behavior. But this was only of minimal importance; the idea of cholera soon got the upper hand, growing constantly and producing greater terror and increasingly frequent attacks. Nevertheless, for years she was cared for at home. But recently, following an attack of influenza, things got so bad that her husband finally decided to regard Justine as insane and to bring her to the Salpêtrière.

The patient obviously exhibits a range of psychological disturbances; she always stays in her room, does no work, spends her time groaning or crying, says nothing, understands little or nothing of what is said to her, etc. etc. But all these disturbances are hard to assess; we will deal with them later when we have understood the main phenomenon that certainly overrides all the others, the idea of cholera.

As soon as we question this person on this touchy subject, she becomes upset, blushes and turns pale, begins to weep, and answers in just a few words: "I'm very afraid of it . . . and have been for a long time . . . I don't know why . . . I don't know what frightens me." She cannot explain better, for she seems immediately to lose consciousness. All her limbs shake, her teeth chatter and are clenched, her arms move in defensive gestures, and her body is bent backward. After several contorsions Justine begins to scream dreadfully; her eyes stay open, fixed as if they were staring at something; her mouth is open and foaming; in the midst of her screams she emits some intelligible words: "Cholera, it's got hold of me, help!" She has cramps and spasms in her legs; she suffocates, turns blue, and vomits either her meals or simply a watery liquid; sometimes she loses control of her bowels. This scene is prolonged and at times goes on for several hours. Then the patient gradually regains consciousness; although she still has spasms in her legs, she feels relieved; she sets her appearance aright and understands vaguely from the mess what had just happened, but she has no precise memory of it. She remains rational for a while but at the slightest allusion that brings back the idea of cholera it all begins again.

How should this whole scene be interpreted? It is an attack of hysteria. This is obviously the common name that readily designates an immense number of phenomena more or less similar to this one, but can the nature of the attack be pinned down more precisely? Studying the patient during her convulsions and screams of terror, one is likely to believe that she is conscious of nothing; one can shout into her ears without getting any response, prick and burn her without any reaction on her part. That is, as is known, an illusion; the conscious phenomena are not ousted, but the minds of patients absorbed by an engrossing idea are no longer capable of perceiving anything or of retaining any memory of them. To attain intelligibility, the patient's perceptions have to be grasped by entering into the dream. When Justine exclaims: "Cholera, it's going to get me," I answer: "Yes, it's holding you by the right leg," whereupon she abruptly draws back her right leg. In this way, with a little patience, one can gradually elicit replies and even converse with the patient: "Where then is your cholera?—There, you can see that blue corpse, how it stinks!" When this point is reached, the mind can slowly be directed to other topics and to chat a little about some matter or other. It is true that the conversation will frequently be interrupted by contorsions and cries of terror, but it will soon become more and more coherent. At the end of the attack Justine no longer recalls the conversation inserted into the delirium. These are phenomena well known under the name of somnambulism that will enable us to move forward in our knowledge of the attack itself. In the first experiments we were obliged to provoke an attack before initiating this state of somnambulism; later we could suppress the opening convulsions almost completely and to induce somnambulism more directly.

This process, which consists of transforming the hysterical attack into somnambulism, is of great theoretical interest and also of practical usefulness. To the many examples we have already reported, we can add a new one. Among other symptoms of hysteria, Gu. presents violent attacks that occur apparently without cause; in addition she has a peculiar horror of the color red and she is obsessed by it to the point of often seeing red spots in front of her and a red tinge over everything. It is impossible to make her go to sleep or to get any information from her about her attacks or her horror of red. During an attack I hear her say: "Take it away; take away the coffin; close it; I don't want to see the head, oh! All this mass of red flowers, take them away." I tell the patient during her attack that I was going to take away the red flowers; she replies: "No, they are still there.—All right! I'll add some violet ones.—Yes please." And so the conversation begins. For a long time it was impossible to induce somnambulism in Gu. other than in this way.

In thus noting that these patients' somnambulism is only a slight transformation of their attack, it is not surprising to encounter again a fact we have often described. In this state the subject remembers perfectly the details of the attack, whereas they are completely forgotten in the waking state. The previous patient, Gu., explains very well during somnambulism how her attack is prompted by the reproduction of an old emotion several years back. She saw her father's corpse just as the coffin was being closed and in each attack she relives this painful sight. She also explains her horror of red by the memory of the flowers on the coffin. The pleasure or the horror that hysterics experience on seeing red or other colors devolves in many cases, as is well known, from the fixed ideas associated with them.

These memories were just as clear during Justine's somnambulism, and they were aroused in the same way. To question her about cholera requires a lot of caution, for this topic tends to trigger the delirium, but all the information can be obtained. Her mind, far from being inactive during the attack, is on the contrary full of many varied images grouped in such a way as to form a unified picture. First there are visual images: two corpses, one of which is visible at the front, "a poor old naked man, green and blue"; sensations of smell, a disgusting odor of putrefaction; auditory images, "the death knell is sounded, cries of cholera, cholera"; kinesthetic images in cramps, screams, vomiting, diarrhea. All these images have a very clear origin, they represent all the feelings this woman has experienced in connection with cholera.

Philosophers have often asked what an idea is, what existed in our minds at the time we had this or that idea. Mr. Ribot recently conducted an inquiry of this kind into general ideas. This patient presents an interesting example of a certain sort of ideas. We see in her what is currently the idea of cholera, developed, so to speak, to the utmost degree of perfection: an ensemble, a system of images taken from all the senses, each of which is clear and complete enough to turn into a reality in the form of hallucinations and movements. Justine's attacks are never a new phenomenon independent of her hypochondriacal preoccupations; it is the same idea of cholera that recurs and turns into a more perfect reality.

The abnormality of this idea during the attacks springs solely from its excessive elaboration. The idea seems to have become segregated from the rest of her life; it is elaborated only when the patient loses consciousness, and it seems to leave no memory behind. In fact, this idea is accompanied by a kind of consciousness that does leave a certain memory, but this is a consciousness and a memory confined to this idea, and it seems to constitute a psychological entity all its own.

The elements aroused by this idea are so numerous and complex that they completely fill the field of consciousness, suppressing every other function and thought. In a sort of vicious circle this sequestration of the idea of cholera contributes even more to enhance its force as the images are freely elaborated in hallucinations and movements. In short, the peculiar features of the attacks are the consequence of the extreme elaboration of the fixed idea.

We can easily verify these connections between the attacks and the idea; if we manage to diminish somewhat the potency of this thought, we will see it reduced to its proper proportions so that it reappears as a simple idea. How to get at such a fixed idea, which had grown so inordinately over twenty-two years despite treatment? We can discuss several psychological therapies that are indicated. Two German authors, Drs. Breuer and Freud, have revived, we are very happy to say, our old studies on subconscious fixed ideas. They have noted, as we did, very serious accidents determined by fixed ideas that the person could not express, of which he/she was even totally unaware. The existence of such ideas could not surface except in attacks, dreams, somnambulism, or unconscious acts and automatic writing. To put it briefly, these ideas remained beneath or rather beyond normal consciousness. Drs. Breuer and Freud therefore concluded that these ideas were dangerous precisely because they were hidden and were not outwardly expressed in an adequate manner. In order to cure the patient, it sufficed to facilitate the outer expression of fixed ideas; when the patient had confessed his fixed idea during somnambulism, he would be cured. In these somewhat theoretical comments there are points that seem quite right. It is true that patients of this type experience great pleasure in expressing their subconscious fixed ideas during somnambulism; they have a curious need to confess. We think it necessary, as we have often said previously, to engage in research into the deep layers of consciousness, and to expose the fixed ideas before trying to cure them. But, unfortunately, that is only the first and the simpler part of the task, for a fixed idea is not cured when it is expressed, quite the contrary. Has not Justine in her innumerable attacks given sufficient voice to her fixed idea about cholera? It hardly needs a word to make her voice it again; can this renewed expression, that is to say, this renewed attack, be regarded as a cure?

Open suggestion, pure and simple prohibition can definitely do more good. We certainly do not believe that it it is enough to say to a demented person, "Be cured," to make him perfectly rational, but we think that in certain cases it is possible to gain some control over the automatic phenomena. As I have often indicated, one can often startle the patient by provoking various hallucinations, by guessing his thoughts from subconscious movements, etc. These first suggestions easily meet with success and arouse no resistance if care is taken not to address the delirium itself at the outset; later an attempt can be made, with some success, to combat the fixed idea itself. These approaches had let me transform the attacks into somnambulism, to stop the elaboration of the idea of cholera, to keep the patient in an almost rational state when she was with me. My influence sometimes persisted when Justine had left me; she came to think of me, to see me appear, when she was about to do something foolish and to stop. But I have to admit that the automatic idea of cholera remained more powerful than my suggestions; she was restrained only for the moment, and after a day or two the attacks about cholera appeared again, a little less violently perhaps, but still quite frequently.

Let us therefore try another slower, more indirect, and more powerful method. The fixed idea seemed to be a construct, a synthesis of a large number of images; instead of getting at it altogether, we must try to *discompose* it, to destroy or transform its elements, and it is likely that then the whole will no longer persist. This is an application to therapeutics of the well known axiom "Divide and conquer." For a while I concentrated on a single feature of the attack, the spasms or the olfactory hallucinations, for example. Various methods of suggestion brought better results here and managed to curtail one or another element of the attack.

Other elements, the visual hallucinations, for example, remained indestructible; instead of suppressing them, I limited myself to modifying them by a kind of *substitution*. So I tried to transform the sight of the corpses, and specifically I devoted several sessions to dressing them. The hallucination of a piece of clothing, then another one, was rather successful; finally the main corpse appeared dressed in the costume of a Chinese general whom Justine had seen at the Exhibition. Success was really achieved when I managed to make the Chinese general stand up and walk; he was no longer terrifying and introduced into the attacks a highly effective comical element. There is no need to enumerate in detail several transformations of the same kind that all had the same aim, to discompose the idea of cholera and to make it tractable. Under this influence the illness changed very quickly; the crises became limited, no longer entailing vomiting and diarrhea; they consisted merely in some screams mixed with bursts of laughter. Curiously, although it is something I have often observed, the crises ceased to occur during the day and came only at night. It seemed justified to suppose that the subconscious idea of cholera was too weak to break into the midst of daytime feelings and ideas, but that it emerged more readily under the cover of sleep. During the night Justine had movements of terror, convulsions, called for help, etc. A further dissociation, the substitution of suggested dreams, reduced these nightmares even more, and the illness seemed considerably attenuated at least in its primary form.

The benefits were, however, minimal, for the illness had undergone a tranformation and appeared just as dreadful in another form. At the time of her major attacks Justine was sick sporadically and at intervals. When the crisis was over, she felt relieved and calm for several hours, sometimes for a day or two. Also, she was not aware of the illness; she knew vaguely she had for a long time been demented by her fear of cholera, but she did not speak about it and hardly thought of it consciously. Indeed, as soon as the idea occurred to her, she remained conscious only for a few minutes and immediately produced an attack with ensuing loss of memory. Since the attacks had disappeared, Justine, although apparently calmer, had in reality become much unhappier. The idea of cholera was no longer powerful or complex enough to suppress it in its entirety; it developed without bringing on an attack, without loss of consciousness and of memory; in short, she remained conscious and constantly obsessed with the illness. "I no longer have," said Justine, "that great fear that used to make me faint and gave me the attacks, but I still think of cholera. I have only *the idea of cholera*, but I have it constantly."

This distinction will seem subtle; nevertheless it is very important from the psychological and the medical point of view. The attack, with its sequence of movements, of psychological disturbances and hallucinations, is only the elaboration of an idea. It is not a new, extraordinary psychological phenomenon; it only shows us all the elements contained in an idea, and probably contained in all our ideas. It shows them in an exaggerated but not a transformed image. This identity between the attack and the idea is demonstrated by the clinical evolution of the illness: as soon as we remove the inordinate power of these elements, they resume their natural form as only a simple idea. On the other hand, our medical classifications favor a categoric separation between those patients who have attacks with loss of consciousness and memory and those who are obsessed with ideas yet retain consciousness and memory. We have already indicated several times the close relationship between those illnesses known as hysteria and psychasthenia, and the similarity of their symptoms psychologically. "Movements through visual images, we said in connection with Marcelle, had a bizarre and rather bad outcome. The movements were indeed carried out somewhat better, but the arms and hands became totally anesthetic; instead of the distraction and the abulia that belong to neurasthenia, I undoubtedly developed hysterical anesthesia." The study of Justine adds another argument: we see here how the attack (the hysterical symptom) can be transformed and become an obsession (psychasthenic symptom); we could show in other instances how frequently the opposite happens when obsessions are transformed into hysterical attacks. It is very likely that at some time or other this transformation occurred in Justine; who was consciously obsessed for years before having the attacks we have noted. This new form assumed by the fixed idea was therefore important and worth pursuing.

What constitutes this idea of cholera now lodged in Justine's mind? Its old component hallucinations have gone; there are no more smells, no more corpses, no more sound of bells. What is left? First of all, a vague emotion, that is to say, a composite of sensations in all parts of her body, coldness, shudders, nausea, etc. But this very genuine emotion seems, according to the patient's repeated testimony, to come second: "Despite myself I think of cholera; I have *the idea*, and that's when I'm afraid."

Irrational feelings and vague terrors are often described in the demented; often, in our opinion, it would be easy through more careful examination to ascertain a more or less conscious fixed idea underlying this emotion without the patient's knowledge. Quite recently in an interesting patient we were able to study such persistent emotions without intellectual manifestations. Cas., since her confinement, is in a state of constant terror. She trembles especially when she sees someone coming toward her, yet she pretends to be afraid of nothing, to think of nothing terrifying. The patient was isolated and examined thoroughly; this first interpretation had to be abandoned. However, Cas. has visual hallucinations during her attacks of terror of which she has only partial memories. During her pregnancy she was beaten by her totally drunk husband, and since then she retains the image of this scene, like a suggestion, that is renewed everytime someone comes into the room. This then is another fixed idea such as we have always seen. We are careful not to deny the existence of pure emotions that have no source in intellectual manifestations; perhaps they can be noted in other illnesses. But we believe that we have the right to demand a more precise analysis of the cases we note.

In the patient we are studying today, in Justine, the feeling of terror seems to be elicited by an idea, as she herself says. But what constitutes this idea whose essential elements seem to have been wiped out? Only one last element remains, and it is easy to find by elimination; it is the *word*. Once attention has been drawn to this area, it is very easy to note the role of language in obsessions. When Justine is still, apparently absorbed in the sewing that she does or does not do, she moves her lips incessantly, muttering a word that is sometimes quite audible, the word *cholera*. She can be prompted to engage in automatic writing and can write different things to order, but she also writes in this way spontaneously, and when she holds a pencil, she scribbles endlessly the word *cholera*. When she does not pronounce or write it, she hears it; it is interesting how this patient has very clear auditory, verbal hallucinations. The voice is an external one in various intonations. "It's several voices mixed, as if it were a crowd, shouting at me. It's my head that says the word *cholera*, not me."

In this respect she has a very clear sense of a doubling of her personality. "When it is I who says the word *cholera*, I realize it perfectly well and I am less afraid, but what makes me sick is when *something* says it despite myself." Here undoubtedly is a patient obsessed by the word, the final remnant of a more complex representation. This obsession was no less serious; it encompasses all her disordered thinking and can gradually retrieve all the old hallucinations.

In order to make this last symptom disappear we resorted to the same methods of division and substitution as previously. By suggestion I transformed the word *cho-le-ra* into the name of the Chinese general. I let her hand write the first syllable *cho* automatically, then I directed her to finish the word *chocolate*. By suggestion I evoked automatic words, words beginning with *co*, like *cotton*, *cocoa*, etc. We hesitate to dwell on the description of these and other methods of the same type that are most useful but may seem rather childish. By way of excuse we will say that we do not yet have many *practical* methods to discompose and destroy memories. In the midst of all these hallucinations, of all these automatic words, Justine came to be completely confused. "What is the word that used to torment me?" she would say; "I've been looking for it for a week; it has got *separated;* I can't *put it together again;* it's *co . . . cotton;* no, it's *cholera*. That's a strange word; what does it mean?"

Certainly there were ups and downs; every now and then an accident, the sight of a dying person, the smell of phenol [a disinfectant], etc., would bring back the idea of cholera by association. But these memories became rarer. Obviously I avoided asking the patient about this topic, and I had strenuously forbidden any conversation that might revive her memories. I was surprised to see how complete her forgetting had become; during the last cholera epidemic in Paris, Justine asked with curiosity what this malady was, and this woman who had gone into such states of delirium at the thought of imaginary cholera laughed at people who were afraid of real cholera. Only very seldom, twice in two years, in connection with accidents to be discussed later, did the fixed idea and the terror seem to return briefly, but they were quickly removed and forgotten.

I felt obliged at an opportune moment to remove various accessory hallucinations that had served to discompose the fixed idea, but in fact they disappeared gradually and spontaneously. This disappearance let the patient acquire again a vague idea of cholera and a very confused memory of her former illness. She speaks of it without emotion, but also without knowing what is really happening.

The treatment that I have just summed up spanned ten months; that is not an excessively long time to destroy so intense a fixed idea that had gone on for twenty years, if the patient could be regarded as cured. Unfortunately we shall have to face many other symptoms that will rob us of our illusions.

II.—The Secondary Fixed Ideas

For the sake of clarity we brought together in the first section all the facts related to the fixed idea of cholera, but in actuality these facts did not exist in isolation. A large number of other pathological phenomena and even other fixed ideas were constantly entangled in it. From the moment when the fixed idea of cholera began to wane, and especially when it disappeared, numerous other threatening fixed ideas surfaced to complicate the study and the patient's treatment in strange ways. We have already designated these phenomena as *secondary fixed ideas;* we have already encountered them often since they form the major obstacle to the treatment of mental illnesses. To forget them would be to fail to acknowledge the illness's essential nature; to limit the malady to a single fixed idea and to imagine that it suffices to remove it by suggestion is to hold a totally mistaken notion of a much more serious and deeper mental disturbance.

These new ideas have the same general characteristics as the first one; they develop inordinately beyond the patient's will and often beyond her consciousness; they give rise to obsessions, impulses, and attacks when they wholly fill the conscious field. It is likely that if they were not halted, they would become as serious and tenacious as the original fixed idea; if one tries to cure them, they undergo incessant transformations and become very numerous and very diversified.

To describe Justine's countless secondary ideas, it is useful to divide them into three categories in accordance with a natural and convenient classification already previously proposed:

1. The secondary fixed ideas by *derivation* or by *association*. Some of these ideas simply seem elements detached from the main fixed idea, or at least easily connected to it by consequential or associative links. However, these fragments of the main idea can develop in isolation and even survive after the disappearance of the original idea. Here is a clear example borrowed from another patient. Ger., a young woman of twenty-eight, was alone present at her mother-in-law's sudden death; she held the dead woman in her arms, and this event unhinged her mind. Ever since, she reproaches herself for her bad attitude toward her mother-in-law, accuses herself of her death, imagines that she killed her, and finally wants to kill herself because she feels guilty of her death. This is the original idea, which, in this instance, has a very clear inception. Appropriate treatment succeeds in suppressing this young woman's fixed idea, and I thought her cured until, a few months later, she was brought back, suffering from an apparently quite new delirium. She wanted to kill her child; a poor little girl of four whom she adored. She despairs of herself for having had this odious thought that made her strike her child, she finds this impulse monstrous and inexplicable. It is, however, a follow-up to the original fixed idea: "The child of a guilty mother, a child that will become guilty like her, must be eliminated," as Ger. very well explains it. The curious thing is that Ger. no longer thinks of killing herself and does not reproach herself; the second idea, although derived from the first, exists quite independently.

Ideas of this kind are very apparent in Justine: for example, we will not be surprised to hear that for the past ten years Justine has refused to eat any fruit or vegetables; that is too obvious a consequence of her cholera idea. But now that the idea of cholera is virtually gone, the patient, without knowing why, obstinately refuses all food: this is a consequence that has become separated from the original idea.

We see her numerous ideas and dreams about death as being in the same category. She dreams that she is unearthing shrouds, undoing them, taking out the corpses, putting them in a wheelbarrow, and carting them to another cemetery. By day she cannot see a hearse without seeing the putrefying corpse in it. Some writers have asserted that those obsessed by fixed ideas do not have hallucinations; we cannot explain this assertion. These patients nearly always first have verbal kinesthetic hallucinations that are a major part of their illness, and very often, in our opinion, they have hallucinations of the other senses when the disintegration of their minds has gone far enough, or when their fixed idea takes the form we have called hysterical. To come back to our patient, she has a dreadful fear of hospitals and makes big detours to avoid passing the entrance to the Saint-Antoine hospital. So when she is finally rid of the idea of cholera, she replaces it with the fixed idea of another sickness and thus has thought of every kind of pathology. She thinks she has cerebral congestion, and in her usual manner she enacts the scene in an attack. When she is found lying on the floor, her limbs flaccid, her breathing shallow, that is quite disturbing, at least the first time. Then it will be heart disease, pleurisy, smallpox, breast cancer that she absolutely wants to have operated, etc. We can regard these ideas as forming a first category, secondary ideas still dependent on the first fixed idea, that of cholera.

2. We note in these patients a second category of secondary fixed ideas that we have already designated as *layered fixed ideas* on account of the peculiar way in which they present to the observer. When a fixed idea has been removed, it is quite surprising to see another one arise that has no connection either with the first idea or with the attendant circumstances. It is an old idea, anterior to the one just treated, that reappears. When this in turn has been removed, there is a third obsession that had existed even earlier so that one is obliged to move backward through all the main fixed ideas that have tormented the patient. This reappearance of old ideas is very typical and very serious in the patient whom we studied first, Marcelle, and it has struck me in other patients too. But in Justine, the secondary ideas of this category are not very important. In her a single idea, that of cholera, had nearly always been dominant without leaving room for other obsessions.

For just a moment she thought herself pregnant again, but this thought did not last; her former anger against her husband surfaced again in a more curious manner. Justine is usually very devoted to her husband and very affectionate; she realizes that she is an insufferable wife and tries to make up for it. All of a sudden she changes her attitude and her expression; she sulks, refusing to speak to him; she turns pale and in a harsh tone begins to reproach him. Soon she becomes excited and hurls all sorts of insults at her husband; she screams as much as in the attacks caused by the fear of cholera; she wants to rush out into the street to look for a lawyer, etc. Gradually the attack subsides, and she has only a very vague memory of what has just gone on. She has to be put into a somnambulistic state in order to learn that the idea arose as she was embracing her husband; she thought she could bite him, and this thought revived the old idea of hatred and divorce. This woman's husband maintains that since the disappearance of the idea of cholera Justine occasionally reverts exactly to the character, the outbursts of rage, the words she used at the beginning of the marriage. This is definitely a fixed idea reappearing.

3. In our opinion, a third category of fixed secondary ideas has to be identified that is more important for our patient and far more interesting for pathological psychology: *accidental* fixed ideas as a result of suggestibility. After Justine had been rid of her old fixed ideas by the methods just described, she was calm for only a short while. Soon she was plagued by a new obsession. This was not an old idea, nor a distant consequence of the original idea of cholera. No, this was a new idea, definitely prompted by some insignificant little life event. A worry, a feeling, a dream, a word overheard by chance would, after a few days' gestation, give rise to a thought that would grow and invade her mind anew.

It is impossible to list all these accidental ideas that tried our patience for a year; here are a few chosen at random. Justine had the idea of throwing herself into the water because water attracted her, to throw herself out of the window because the house leaned to one side; the idea of strangling her dog and hanging her birds; the idea of throwing her food on the floor or at the heads of people coming into the room. She obstinately refused to put on a hat when she went out, to change her underclothes (she puts on clean underwear in her husband's presence because he forces her to, and as soon as he turns his back, she undresses and puts the dirty underwear on again); she does not want any light for fear of setting her dress or the house on fire; she refuses to buy anything at the market for fear of being robbed; she refuses to do the housekeeping or to touch anything in her room. She is obsessed by the idea that her piano is no good and not worth the minimal price paid for it (frightful scenes for weeks on end); she is tortured by the memory of having refused her husband, ten years ago, a cup of an herbal tea; by regret for a small bottle that she broke and mourns day and night. Then comes the fear of lying and that she lies all the time, hatred of an apprentice, inordinate love for a neighbor's small dog, etc., etc. Instead of a single, unique fixed idea that had dominated her for twenty years, we find her facing a swarm of little fixed ideas that are incessantly transformed and renewed.

In order to show the seriousness of these accidental secondary ideas, I will dwell on some of them that took a particularly interesting form. Engrossed in a piece of music that she is studying, Justine notices that she does not see clearly, that there is black dust in front of her eyes. Looking at this dust more carefully, she notices with astonishment that it is the musical notes of her piece that are always before her and prevent her from seeing well enough to go out into the street: another visual hallucination. She has read a few pages of a novel by Eugène Sue in which one of the characters is very proud. She gets so much under this character's skin that she hears people reproaching her for her behavior and her pride: an auditory hallucination. She is afraid of lying; this common idea of the lie in these patients stems no doubt from the disturbance in their attention, but in Justine this idea becomes manifest in an inner voice that accuses her of dishonesty. It is the same voice, as the patient herself comments, that once used to say "cholera"; the old kinesthetic verbal hallucinations are recognizable.

In other instances, fixed ideas prompt subconscious movements. Absorbed in a change in her lodging, Justine dreams every night of moving; she moves around while asleep and wakes in the morning with arms and legs in spasms. These contractures are especially interesting; they are clearly systemic. Not all her muscles are taut to the same extent; they are taut to different degrees so as to maintain the limb in a rigid but expressive position. Her arms are half bent in front of her as if she were carrying a heavy object; one of her legs is extended at the thigh with the foot turned toward the leg; the other leg is half bent: it is the position taken by the lower limbs when going upstairs. The spasms are released during somnambulism when Justine can explain and modify her dream. She often had spasms of this kind as a result of the dreams she had at night and even by day. She dreams that she is climbing a tree and her hands stay clawed; she dreams of her piano and of the difficulty of reaching an octave, and her two hands stay stuck, her fingers stiff and stretched to the maximum to reach the octave.

These systemic spasms are not seen often, although in reality they are not very rare, but usually they do not maintain the same form for long. Gradually all the muscles contract more and more and the limb takes on the classical position of a generalized contracture. Subconscious phenomena are, as we have shown, very invasive; they do not remain limited, but quickly grow, suppressing and modifying other apparently separate psychological facts. This is how the anesthesias spread, somnambulistic amnesias increase, and the moments preceding the second state are forgotten like the somnambulism itself. So as to see subconscious phenomena and particularly systemic spasms very clearly, they have to be observed from their inception.

These accidental ideas also produce attacks, and we will report just one accident that caused us a lot of worry. Justine, who seemed quite well, had been to the hospital in the morning to take a shower; she came back with that somber look that always presaged a storm but could not explain what was bothering her. At about three o'clock in the afternoon she came in a furious rage, armed with a knife, and ran at her husband to strike him. In a moment of consciousness she shouted: "Run away; I'm going to kill you," then she fell into a delirium. It took three men to restrain her. Informed immediately, I was very affected by this madness, that I had tried to curb, becoming more and more serious, and I thought an immediate commitment [to an asylum] necessary. However, I was able to note that this new fixed idea, although apparently more frightening, was no different from the others. In the morning at the shower the attendant had told of a minor happening: a patient she knew had been shut into a room in an asylum because she wanted to kill her husband. That was enough; Justine had thought about these words all day, then her mind was swamped with this one idea—to kill her husband with a knife—and this idea had been the core of an attack, just as the idea of cholera had previously been. This dangerous fixed idea could fortunately be easily dislodged, and Justine regained her tranquility at least for a while.

It is in fact easy to note that all these secondary ideas, especially those in the last category, could be dislodged without much trouble. A session of somnambulism, an initial image, some suggestions, some dissociations, have readily restored reason. This held especially for ideas of short anterior duration. Fixed ideas are like spasms; Dr. Charcot has very rightly pointed out that spasms should not be left to last; nor must fixed ideas be left to develop. The closer to their origin that they are addressed, the easier it is to discompose and to destroy them.

But this comment did not advance our patient's cure. What was the good of acquiring the ability quickly to remove a fixed idea if she took up another one a few moments later? This infestation of fixed ideas, like parasites on a dying tree, is her most serious characteristic. Her

mind seemed to have been profoundly deranged by the first obsession and was now unable to resist the development of the slightest
idea implanted into her. A somewhat strange comparison lets us
understand this state and its dangerous nature. It is known that our
organs are normally very little open to infections; although numerous, diverse microbes are incessantly deposited on our orifices, they
hardly get in, and in the body's interior the mucus remains unin-
fected. There are many reasons for this resistance to infectious organ-
isms, but under some circumstances the body is beaten. A special,
particularly dangerous kind of microbe introduces infection into the
organ. From that moment onward a very curious phenomenon
occurs that has been well illuminated by Dr. Jules Janet in connection
with a special organ. Once the original infection is healed, the organ
does not return to its former state of resistance and immunity; it
remains, on the contrary, sometimes for a long time, in a *state of receptivity;* that it to say, it can easily at any minute be infected by some
common microbe or other that had no effect on it before. These secondary infections in organic pathology seem to me rather analogous
to the secondary fixed ideas in psychological pathology. In both we
see that the illness is not over with the infection or with the original
fixed idea; the remaining receptivity gives rise to incessantly reiterated relapses. Each of these relapses is dangerous: it is easy to see,
returning to our patient, that each new fixed idea can gain strength
and grow, and that it would quickly turn into an illness as serious as
the first one. It is, moreover, not impossible that one of these new
ideas might by association revive the first one and thrust the patient
back into the state from which she had emerged. The cure, which had
cost us so much trouble, is therefore quite compromised and seems
not to have been as complete as one might have hoped.

III.—Suggestibility and Abulia
[Loss of ability to perform voluntary actions or to make decisions]

The accidental fixed ideas just studied are not a new phenomenon
for us; they are wholly identical to phenomena already fully analyzed
in experimental studies of suggestion. In both we find the same development of the sensory and motor elements contained in an idea, the
same separation of thought from normal consciousness. It is easy to
verify this supposition in our patient.
    Ever since we first knew her, Justine has been amazingly sug-
gestible. If one of her arms was raised, she forgot it in this strange

position; soon the limb even went into spasms *in situ,* thereby giving us an experimental reproduction of systemic spasms. A word, during her normal waking, prompted all the hallucinations or determined dreams that would be accompanied by spontaneous hallucinations. These ideas suggested to her develop strongly and quite beyond her normal personality. It would be unwise to get in her way or to try to stop her when I had put a suggestion to her; she became as stubborn, as violent, as little conscious as during her natural attacks. So it is easy to prompt all sorts of subconscious acts, of totally automatic writing and even of speech that she utters without being aware of it and without being able to stop just as she once used to mutter the word *cholera.* The production of these accidental fixed ideas (a word heard by chance, a piece of a newspaper she has read, etc.) is the same process as in suggestion so that these two phenomena may ultimately be subsumed under the same word: it is this woman's extreme suggestibility that gives rise to her constantly renewed fixed ideas.

Some writers have without hesitation asserted that suggestion is not a phenomenon peculiar to certain patients and that we are all suggestible. This opinion no doubt stems from some linguistic confusion, for under the name of *suggestion* all the mechanical phenomena of thought, memory, association of ideas, habits, etc., have been confused. But if the word *suggestion* is limited to a precise sense, that is, the complete and automatic development of certain ideas beyond personal will and consciousness, we will become convinced, we believe, that suggestion is clearly a pathological phenomenon. In any case, the example of Justine strikes us as instructive: here is a truly suggestible person, and the consequences of her suggestibility have been seen. Are we all like this woman? Are we at every moment obsessed by all the fixed ideas that suggestion can prompt in us? Obviously we shall have to concede that there is some difference between suggestibility in a normal person and that in our patient; at least a considerable difference of degree will surely be recognized. It is this difference that we shall try to understand in researching in the other disturbances of brain functions the reason for this abnormal suggestibility.

Many other disturbances were in fact mingled with the fixed ideas we described separately. Let us point first of all to certain accidental, transitory phenomena that could also be called attacks, but that seem to us quite distinct from the attacks described above. From time to time, especially during phases of uneasiness and fatigue, or after work that required close attention, Justine would stay motionless, her eyes fixed and her mouth half open. She would stay like this for hours on end; when she was called, she would reply with meaningless words or with questions: "Where am I? I don't understand. . . . I don't know anymore . . . my head is empty . . . I am dead." Instead of furiously resisting, as she usually did in her attacks, she would allow herself to be guided and would obey very simple orders: "Come and sit down. . . ." But she immediately reverted to her numbness. This *stupor* lasted just a few hours; only once, to my knowledge, did it last two days. If one seeks out, by the methods already described, what fills her mind during these attacks, no precise idea emerges, merely very vague dreams, "people who move, who hit each other; passing overturned carriages with horses whose hooves are in the air." Most often even there is no dream, Justine thinks of nothing; perceives and understands nothing, she has "an empty head" and the feeling "of no longer living, of being dead."

This attack of stupor is very important; it is in many respects identical to those attacks of mental confusion just described after infectious diseases. But here this mental confusion is not basic; it is a momentary exaggeration of a general state of weakness in this chronic patient, and this absence of perception is only the final extent of the disturbances of attention that have persisted throughout her life. The various syndromes that are described under the names of neurasthenia, abulia, mental confusion, or stupor seem to us to be varying degrees of the same psychological derangement, and under different influences the patient can easily switch from one to another.

We will therefore find in Justine all the symptoms we have described in other patients under the name of abulia. It is interesting to see their features again and to note that they go hand in hand with fixed ideas and suggestibility. We will study these phenomena in her will, her attention, her memory, and her perception of feelings.

Up to now we have seen Justine only in her attacks, and we have found her only agitated and violent. She is quite different between attacks, mainly much calmer, for she has long been incapable of doing anything. She is like a child who makes no decisions and does not resist, acting only under the impetus of those around her and often unable to obey them despite her efforts to do so: "I would much like to work, but I haven't the heart to get up, to wash. . . ." To get out of her bed, her chair, is an inhuman task. As we know, once she has begun work, she can continue it indefinitely, but cannot interrupt it and begin again. She stayed a whole day sewing buttonholes without being able to get up to go and eat. We will not dwell on these facts, nor on her slowness and the hesitancy of her voluntary actions as against the vehemence of her compulsive actions; these are already well known facts.

Her attention is nil, and this disrupts all knowledge of the present. Of course, Justine reads without understanding; that is a most typical symptom in these patients. "Between me and your newspaper there is a monstrous obstacle, a thick fog." Let us not take these words too literally: she can see clearly and she can spell out the letters well; it is the synthesis of the words of which she is incapable. This attention gap is manifest even in her perception of objects; she does not know the people who come to see her and asks her husband the purpose of the most common objects. She understands language poorly, has no confidence in what is said to her, and eventually doubts her own words: "Have I said something silly? . . . I must have lied, etc." Her imprecise perceptions surprise her, and she complains of no longer seeing things as she used to: "The world has sure changed. . . . Things are no longer recognizable . . . a fog surrounds things, and people speak through a wall." It is really curious to note how much these patients are alike: "the emptiness in the head, the fog, the wall" are typical expressions that can be regarded as symptoms, for they recur in exactly the same way in all studies.

In memory there are very complex disturbances; certain amnesias are clearly systemic: for example, Justine forgets her husband's face when he is away for a few hours, even failing to recognize pictures of him. We have already described some of these systemic amnesias pertaining to language. Justine loses the memory that would enable her to mobilize certain words; she hears them but cannot pronounce them: her husband has to articulate them before her so that she sees the movement of his lips and tries to reproduce them. When she is alone and wants to pronounce these words, she has to evoke the visual image of his lips in order to copy the movement. She is very forgetful of writing and suddenly no longer knows how to spell a word; she writes it in a weird spelling or bypasses it completely. These little forgettings of words or writing on the part of hysterics are interesting from the clinical point of view, for they sometimes simulate the typical forgetfulness of paralytic dementia for which they are liable to be mistaken.

Other localized amnesias were produced by the attacks and by somnambulism. All the phenomena clustered around the unconscious dreams were, so to speak, induced by them and connected to this second existence. These amnesias, however, appeared in Justine with interesting irregularity. Forgetting was complete on waking from somnambulism, but on the next and the following days some memories of the second state reappeared in wakefulness. This return of memories can be explained, case by case, in different ways; here we believe that it is due to the fact that the patient dreamed in the night following the somnambulistic session and partly remembered her dreams, which become a sort of intermediary between somnambulism and waking.

But the most important disturbance of memory was that which we have called *continued amnesia.* Justine remembers old happenings well, especially those of her childhood, but she recalls recent things badly. This forgetting became obvious one day: her husband had bought her a piano; for a long time she would stop by this piano without knowing where it came from: "I know the other furniture well, but where does this piano come from? Who put it there?" Despite apparently great efforts, sustained over several days, she could not manage to learn a few lines by heart and to repeat them. These amnesias existed only for the conscious person: memories, as is known, persist subconsciously. During her attacks and her somnambulism, Justine recited very well the pieces of poetry that she had tried to learn. This kind of amnesia is connected to disturbances in attention and conscious perception; we cannot come back to this study.

Finally this psychological flaw appeared in a more decisive, simpler manner in the disturbances of conscious sensitivity. Various anesthesias of the senses existed at the beginning and were reproduced in various circumstances: complete anesthesia for pain, touch, and movement on the left side; anesthesia of the tongue, loss of taste, loss of the pharyngeal reflex, almost total loss of smell, reduction of the visual field to 70 on the right and 35 on the left. But it has to be admitted that these anesthesias were subject to extreme variations and were modified by all sorts of influences. They seemed to disappear as soon as the fixed ideas diminished and would reappear with each new obsession. This anesthesia corresponds exactly to the type we have described as anesthesia by distraction; it shows us how more stable anesthesias are formed in other hysterics.

Most often a reduction, a disturbance in the sensations, rather than their complete suppression, was noted. These problems were particularly strange for the visual sense and prompt interesting comments.

The first of these visual disturbances is often connected, in my opinion, to the fact known as asthenopia [subjective symptom of ocular fatigue or discomfort]. When the patient stares at something, when for example she tries to read and understand, she can see clearly for only a short time; after about two minutes, she complains of pain in her eyes, at the top of her nose; she has tears in her left eye, then in the right one; she sees less and less, and finally is in nearly total darkness. This blockage of her vision lasts for approximately two minutes; then vision comes back in the right eye, then in the left. If the patient goes on reading, the same problem recurs within a few minutes. Is a phenomenon of this kind essentially visual, is it due to disturbances in the eye itself? We do not think so. In fact we note something very similar for the sense of hearing when it is used with willed attention. We ask the patient to listen to the sound of a clock or a metronome; she can do it for only a minute and a half. Then she begins to groan, to complain of pain in her ear until she can hear absolutely nothing; hearing comes back gradually only to disappear once more if the patient tries to pay attention. Besides, this phenomenon occurs solely under certain conditions: feeling must be attentive and willed in order for her to tire so quickly. When the patient chats with us with her eyes open, she complains of nothing, yet for half an hour she has seen all that was happening; what is more, when she holds a book and scans it with her eyes without trying to understand what she is reading, she does not become blind in a couple of minutes. She can really see, since in somnambulism afterward she can summarize the content of this page. This asthenopia is thus a special manifestation of the weakness of attention that cannot understand and synthesize visual phenomena except for a short time and that rapidly tires.

Another alteration in her vision is also connected to the inadequacy of her attention, namely, the modifications in her visual field. Justine's visual field is subject to extreme variations; it shrinks enormously as soon as the patient feels physically or mentally tired, and especially as soon as she is obsessed by fixed ideas. I have shown elsewhere that the seriousness of this patient's fixed ideas can be ascertained simply by her visual field. Even at times when the visual field is extensive and seems normal, it nevertheless shows a latent alteration that can be exposed only experimentally.

At the middle of the apparatus I fix a piece of paper on which there are either a few phrases in small writing or some numbers. I put the subject in the desired position to measure his visual field and I ask him to look only at the middle but still to read the letters and to do an arithmetical sum on the numbers. When his attention is fully directed at this task, which usually happens after a few instants, I move a stick with a little white object on the perimeter, at the outer corner of the eye being examined, going from the periphery toward the center; I hold it for a moment at a point I know to be in the subject's visual field, at forty degrees for example, then I remove it. At the same time I interrupt the subject's work and ask him whether he has seen the signal moving in a circle. Depending on his reply, I begin the same procedure again, letting the signal move further out or bringing it toward the center. So the subject's visual field can be determined while his attention is fixed.

We have shown in this experiment that attention reduces the normal person's visual field little, but it considerably reduces sick people's visual field. Under these circumstances Justine goes from ninety to thirty degrees, and sometimes to twenty. The power of personal perception is so slight that she cannot focus on one point without losing sight of the others, and this happens because there are more details to see at the center that the peripheral visual field reduces. This shrinking of the visual field by attention is also part of a group of facts of a similar kind, for it is easy to note a passing anesthesia of all the other senses when the patient pays attention to a particular one: this reduction of the ability to synthesize, this shrinking of field of consciousness related clearly to the number of *simultaneous* phenomena, whereas in the foregoing observations on asthenopia it seemed related to the length of time, to the number of *successive* phenomena that could be consciously perceived.

Finally we will only indicate a last ocular disturbance that would require lengthy investigations, namely, diplopia [double vision] in one or both eyes. The patient sees double; but what is astonishing and contrary to all optical laws, she sees double even when she has only one eye open. Without going again into delicate discussions connected to this one-eyed diplopia, we will recall only the conclusions. "The difficulty in accommodation, which accompanies one-eyed diplopia and that has been studied by Dr. Parinaud, is the point of departure for an illusion; the patient in reality sees disturbances and not doubles of the objects that are not exactly at the point where his eye is accommodated. It is through a habitual hallucination, through a fixed idea that true diplopia is caused." But from where does such a peculiar fixed idea come? It comes, in the present case, from a two-eyed diplopia that is genuine and among the most interesting symptoms for the psychological analysis of these patients.

When Justine has both eyes open, she sees two images, each one of which is supplied by one eye; this can be established by covering one eye with colored glass: one of the images is red while the other remains white. This diplopia is due partly to a defect in the convergence of optical axes and to a genuine, passing strabismus [cross-eyedness]. But this defect of convergence and this strabismus themselves have a deep cause, that is, the defect in the fusion, the synthesis of the diverse images supplied by the two eyes. This feature is very widespread in hysterics: often it is hidden as in the case of Justine. The patients soon suppress the images supplied by one eye, they leave them in the subconscious, and although they have both their eyes open, they see consciously with only one. They instinctively substitute monocular for binocular vision. It is easy to ascertain this by means of a quite simple little experiment: while they read a book, a pencil placed vertically before their two open eyes prevents them from reading certain letters; this would not happen if they were using both eyes. As Dr. Parinaud has elegantly shown, binocular vision can properly be regarded as human and its loss considered a degeneration, a return to animals' monocular vision. It can be noted in particular that this disturbance of vision wholly confirms the ideas we have always expressed about these patients' sensations, the defect in synthesis, the dissociation of functions that surfaces here in a more precise manner than anywhere else perhaps.

These are, briefly summarized, the principal disturbances that we note in our patient's will, attention, memory, and feelings. These problems in diverse functions combine, as might be supposed, to produce an overall change in character and personality. Justine herself noticed it and would incessantly repeat the stereotypical phrase: "I am changed, I no longer recognize myself." Her character was mainly childlike: this forty-year-old woman is as astonished and naive as a small child; she wants to be played with, to be amused; she argues interminably about trifles like a ten-year-old. But in addition she exhibits, too, often quite inexplicably bizarre behavior, all the contradictions typical of hysterics' conduct and stance. Her mind is surprisingly subtle, yet she is stupid, unable to understand the simplest things; her sensitivity seems deep; affection, remorse, all her feelings seem exalted; yet her indifference and insensitivity are also absolute. This woman is herself astonished at her own character: "How can I dissolve into tears for a piece of music and have such an arid heart! I'm basically very good, I wish everyone well, and I do no one any good." We have already tried many times to explain these contradictions; we have perhaps pointed to certain aspects of the solution, the difference between past, acquired intelligence; and current intelligence, between automatic functioning and the mind's personal, conscious functioning. But looking more closely at these always interesting characteristics, we see again and again new difficulties and questions.

We cannot end this study without mentioning the physiological problems that went along with these mental disturbances; they are also very typical and occur in most of the patients of this type.

We will not dwell on her digestive problems, although at first sight they may seem considerable. Justine, who ate very irregularly, had a stressful digestion, with vomiting and alternating diarrhea and extremely obstinate constipation. However, her stomach was not dilated and showed no noteworthy changes; her problems seemed to be very directly connected to her fixed idea of cholera and to her diet; they disappeared very quickly and did not seem to go hand in hand with the other symptoms of her mental state.

On the other hand, the problems of her total nutrition were terribly strange: as in Marcelle, we see first dry, flaky skin; broken nails; hair loss; etc. But we are also struck by a peculiar obesity; this varied, increasing during her phases of serious illness and decreasing when Justine gave up her fixed ideas, resumed her willpower and some interest in work. It had been like this, as will be seen, from the patient's childhood onward.

The circulatory and especially the vasomotor problems were more clear-cut. Ecchymoses [purplish patches] appeared on her limbs as a result of the contractures caused by dreams, red spots on her chest and face were often pronounced, congestion of her face alternated with sudden pallor, etc. The red blotches on her nose, her ears, and beneath her eyes are very common in all neurasthenics and contribute to their characteristic physiognomy. But in Justine they were so variable as to seem connected to the patient's unstable emotions.

For long her menstruation was painful and scant; besides, at this time there was always a marked rise in her symptoms. Not only did her old fixed ideas recur intensively at each period, but that was also the point in time when the patient produced new fixed ideas. It is hardly possible to overstate women's suggestibility at the time of their periods. This is, in my opinion, the unrecognized source of many nervous and mental illnesses.

The general disturbance of the nervous system also becomes manifest in physical symptoms that we feel obliged to mention. It is well known that mostly anesthesia and hysterical paralysis do not affect the reflexes, because they are often only psychological symptoms, but apart from the anesthesia and the paralysis, we believe that changes in the reflexes can occur in these patients in connection with the general exhaustion of the nervous system. Not only did Justine lose her pharyngeal reflex, which is common, but she also showed very diminished, almost absent patellar reflexes. In addition, *her pupils are asymmetrical,* that on the right far more contracted than that on the left side, an asymmetry that seems to me due to the slowness and inadequacy of the left pupillary reflex. What is more, since the patient is unable to stand with her eyes shut, she has vertigo, and the memory difficulties we have described, many people would be inclined toward a very serious diagnosis. That would, however, be mistaken, a conviction we have reached after long observation. These changes in her reflexes vary, and, surprisingly, the pupils become symmetrical as soon as the fixed ideas are removed and her mind takes control. Moreover, as is known, nothing is easier than to confuse these hysterical or neurasthenic states with incipient general paralysis. It is therefore useful to recall once more by an example that even the problems with the reflexes and the asymmetry of the pupils cannot be decisive diagnostic signs.

We will not attempt to assess which of these psychological and physiological disturbances are fundamental and determine the others; that is a totally idle pursuit. All these phenomena are equally important, they form a unity of which nothing must be ignored, they are all manifestations of a single basic change that will probably remain for long unknown. The only thing that seems to us important to note is that these disturbances share a common character, the dissociation of the functions, the loss of unity, the diminishment of that constant synthesis of which the life of the mind consists.

It is precisely this global nature that explains the suggestibility and the proliferation of the fixed ideas. They do not develop completely because they develop in isolation. The entire mind and body no longer come to participate in each phenomenon, as in normal persons; the dispersal leads to a loss of equilibium and to the exaggerated development of one part that becomes like a parasite.

IV. Evolution of the Mind

Knowledge of the above facts must modify our ideas on the treatment of the illness. We can undoubtedly modify or even suppress this or that fixed idea with greater or lesser ease, but we will let a most dangerous mental state continue in which innumerable other fixed ideas will develop, ideas sometimes more dangerous than the original one, replacing what we have suppressed. The very power of our suggestions, which seems felicitous to us, is an indication of the mind's profound dissolution, and the easier the cure appears to be, the sicker the mind is in reality. To suppress fixed ideas one after the other as they appear is to condemn oneself to an interminable task and to expose the patient to all sorts of dangers. Together with the local accident represented by the fixed idea, the general state of mind must be treated that allows the formation of fixed ideas and underlies suggestibility.

It is wrong to nurture illusions about the very mediocre power of therapeutics, and we have to admit that we have very scant knowledge of how to treat these nervous exhaustions that are the origin of so many accidents. The treatments that have been proposed are innumerable, and their large number is no proof of their worth. No doubt various tonic treatments can be useful in certain cases, but in the present case we note that the patient has used and abused all possible treatments over the past twenty years, and, what is more, that the use of medications increases her inclination to hypochondria. Since the medications' useful effects do not compensate, in our opinion, for their bad moral influence, we gave them up altogether. We maintained only hydrotherapy, whose good influence we have always valued in cases of this kind. But Justine has been getting showers since the age of fifteen without being cured, so that this procedure should not be expected to provide more than quite relative help.

Is it easier to treat this mental insufficiency by psychological methods, and, especially, can one use here, as previously, the methods of somnambulism and suggestion? This is sometimes effective when the mind, rid of its fixed idea, spontaneously resumes its activity, but when the mind remains deeply ill after the disappearance of the obsession, we do not believe that suggestions can cure it. Some writers believe that willpower and freedom can be suggested; in our opinion, that is an error in reasoning and observation that we have often pointed out. The patient to whom the suggestion is made will pretend to resist you by obeying, but she will not be really free; on the contrary, suggestion fosters automatic and subconscious activity and reduces the remnants of voluntary efforts. The patients very quickly assume a strange and dangerous habit: they are astonished at nothing; they accept hallucinations, unconscious movements, and the most bizarre turmoil. This is because they have absolute confidence in their magnetizer [hypnotist] and believe him to be in control of and responsible for all that goes on in their minds. This indifference, this renunciation of any personal control, is highly dangerous and contributes more than a little to increasing these patients' fundamental abulia. In short, suggestion, like every dangerous medication, is useful in certain cases: it can serve to reach and to suppress fixed ideas that have become subconscious and are utterly beyond the patients' control, thus preventing any restoration of mental activity, but apart from this role, it is extremely harmful, for it can only increase the mental disintegration that underlies all accidents.

We are therefore obliged to seek a psychological treatment that acts on the essential points, increasing the capacity for mental synthesis and of the faculties dependent on it, willpower, judgment, and attention. Do methods exist to achieve this? Have pedagogues established treatments for attention? We regret not knowing them, and we have been reduced to invoking the most banal methods, namely, education and exercise, to develop an inadequate faculty.

Cerebral work in deranged persons raises a problem that is sometimes quite tricky. Often the inclination is to believe that these tired, overloaded minds need rest, and they are granted total inactivity, which they gladly accept. This view may often be the right one; in many cases of acute neurasthenia, obviously brought on by excessive cerebral work, as complete rest of the brain as possible will become necessary. But is this also valid for those chronic neurasthenics who have in fact done nothing for many years? Is such prolonged cerebral inertia not as dangerous as the indefinite immobilization of a limb after a sprain or a fracture? That is what we have thought and have wanted to verify by means of experimentation. For several years we have been trying to subject a number of patients, notably Justine, to a method of treatment that consists of making them do regular brain work like children at school. Methods of this kind have often been proposed, especially by Legrand du Saulle, who also noted the effects of cerebral work on doubters and obsessives, but this method was, if I am not mistaken, used and understood differently. Legrand du Saulle considered work as a means to distract patients from their obsessions, so he sought to fill their minds with various interesting sights. Hence the recommendation to travel, which often strikes us as a prejudice; too many new sights all too frequently tire these people's attention and are not consciously perceived. We regard work not as a distraction but as an exercise that increases the capacity for mental synthesis that alone is an effective counteragent to suggestibility and fixed ideas.

Thus we would like to avoid work that can be carried out mechanically without paying much attention; we would like to make the patients do only work that requires judgment and the need to combine. We would also like to grade this work according to the length of attention it demands and the number of factors that have to be combined. Perhaps it might in this way be possible to expand the range of consciousness, to give the mind the power to hold several ideas simultaneously, to combine them and to contrast one from another.

There is always, and especially in the medical field, an enormous difference between theory and practice. We cannot convey the difficulties we encountered in this strange endeavor to get a deranged forty-year-old woman to school. It was difficult to find the appropriate type of work, even more so to make her do it. Then the work was carried out otherwise than it should be; it was done automatically without useful results; Justine read without understanding what she read, could recite what she had learned only in the somnambulistic state, etc.

If the work was done properly, it became extremely onerous, causing headaches or serious accidents, attacks, sleepiness, stupors of up to forty-eight hours, that did not reassure witnesses of the treatment's efficacy. It needed real obstinacy to continue this experiment for two years. On the one hand, I resorted to all the resources of suggestion, which here came into play again, in order to convince the patient to do this work; on the other hand, Justine's husband, a very intelligent man, devoted to this poor woman, showed great patience and skill in carrying through this strange medical prescription.

We were able at first to get a few minutes of conscious attention without accident, bringing the patient to explain a few lines, to do a sum, etc. Then the work could be extended to half an hour, an hour a day without problems. Old memories that seemed to have been wiped out suddenly reappeared and facilitated the task; after several days of fruitless effort, Justine would suddenly discover that she knew how to do multiplication. Little literary compositions were written, and—surprise, surprise!— she could recite her lessons in the waking state. No doubt, from time to time mishaps occurred; Justine would suddenly become stupid or would forget what she had been learning for three months, and we had to begin all over again. But a new kind of work that we made her do brought an astonishing result: Justine began to learn the piano and develped a passion for music. The natural attention of which Ribot so rightly speaks melded with the acquired attention so that her education made great progress.

This progress became manifest in an interesting manner that we have already described in another patient: it was not gradual and continuous, but in abrupt fits and starts. One day the patient had several good hours during which she understood everything, no longer felt any malaise, and declared herself totally cured. "I find myself again as I was in my childhood; I haven't been like this for years." Then abruptly everything relapsed sometimes for a longer, at other times for a shorter while. These phases, very analogous to Marcelle's "clear moments," were repeated and prolonged for hours, then for days. In about the past year, these clear moments last for at least three weeks and disappear only during her periods.

Now that these phases of moral health are extensive, the overall outcome of her education can be assessed. Justine has acquired some skills; she can do the accounts for a small business, and read easy piano pieces in a passable manner; she is very proud of these skills but we did not dwell on them. The really interesting finding is that most of the symptoms of abulia have been radically modified. Her physical and intellectual activity has largely been recuperated; the patient works constantly in her home, making herself useful, and during the hours devoted to cerebral work seeks to resolve worthwhile problems, whereas previously she could not understand three lines of a newspaper. Her doubts have disappeared, her memory is normal, and the anesthesias can be noted only very rarely. Her visual field still shrinks according to the level of her attention, but much less so than previously, and the diplopia has gone. The patient is well aware of all these changes and is astonished to realize things she had not understood for many years; she feels more capable of affection, and happier in every way.

What is more surprising is that her physical health reflects these modifications in her mental health. She eats and digests properly, and yet, although she eats much more than previously, she is losing weight: she has dropped from 197 kilos to 169, that is, in four months she has lost 27 kilos. This inexplicable fact seems to confirm our earlier comment: that her obesity was connected to pathological nervous phenomena. Her skin is no longer dry, and her color quite different. One might smile at these comments and find it at least strange that this woman's hair grows again because she writes literary pieces and plays the piano. We will simply reply that we are relating facts and that a fact is never ridiculous. On the other hand, it must be noted that this woman was in a continuous delirium; incessantly presented vasomotor disturbances together with emotional agitation; that she slept and ate in a most irregular way. As of now, thanks to cerebral work, we have been able to institute a perfectly correct and calm lifestyle. Is it so astonishing that her physical health and her nutritional state reflect the effect of these modifications? What is more interesting and what is the special object of our research is the phenomenon of suggestibility and of fixed ideas. What has become of them in the midst of all these changes? The modifications in suggestibility are difficult to appreciate because the patient can sense, according to the tone of the suggestion, whether we want to be obeyed or not, so she can disobey out of obedience. We have, however, tried to experiment in the correct manner. We have never let the patient suspect our research; from time to time we have tried suggestions in the waking state and noted the results without telling her. We concede that our research is not perfect; nevertheless, here are our results. The suggestibility, the subconscious acts, the mental disintegration have not disappeared completely: somnambulism can still be induced and this denotes to us the persistence of a pathological streak. At certain times, for instance, during her periods, the suggestibility is nearly as strong as formerly. But in more favorable phases the suggestibility has decreased enormously and most of the suggestions no longer "take." The patient does as she is asked, but out of voluntary obedience, with her personal consent, not as an automatic act. If Justine remains susceptible to suggestions from us, who naturally have assumed great power over her mind, she shows, by contrast, far more resistance to ideas put forward by others. She is no longer vulnerable to suggestion by just any word or incident. She feels the oncome of a fixed idea and knows how to stop it herself: quite often reading a page or playing the piano has dissipated obsessions that would previously have brought on a month of delirium. In the past year she has had only one serious attack, and even it is almost excusable. A little dog of which she was very fond was run over right under her eyes; she lost consciousness and again produced one of her old attacks with a fixed idea and delirium, but the attack passed without after-effects, and the next day everything had blown over. This recovery, partial though it is, seems to us in accordance with the view that her suggestibility was connected to her abulia and mental disintegration.

It thus seems that the stringent education of her mind exerted a good influence; she has not been able to banish the tenacious old fixed ideas, but her suggestibility has decreased and she can prevent new fixed ideas from developing. The present outcome is satisfactory, but we have already had too many disappointments to be overconfident, and we have to evaluate and assess this apparent recovery in its true light. That is what we will do by surveying the evolution of this illness as a whole.

V.—Evolution of the Illness.
Personal and Hereditary Antecedents

In order to understand a thing well, an attempt must be made to go back to its origins: what is the beginning, the cause, of an illness like the one we have just been studying? A considerable part of the symptoms devolved from the outset on the idea of cholera; where did this idea come from? As we have seen, from a feeling that Justine experienced when she went with her mother to bury the dead and she saw the corpses of those who had succumbed to cholera. Should this reply be regarded as an explanation? Does this whole long illness, this whole mental transformation, stem from this simple little accident?

Obviously not: we have seen that fixed ideas germinate in the mind only thanks to a quite special state of suggestibility. And we know that this suggestibility does not exist constantly in all healthy human beings. The first fixed idea will undoubtedly unhinge the mind and leave it open to far greater suggestibility, but at the outset already there had to be some weakness that allowed the first idea to unfold. So we have to go beyond this idea of cholera and find the explanation of the suggestibility itself and this mind's weakness at synthesizing.

We will come upon a second reply that also encompasses part of the truth and that today is assuming growing importance. Justine, it will be remembered, had typhoid fever; now, infectious diseases, particularly this one, are very often apt profoundly to alter the nervous system and especially the brain; they cause convulsions and delirium and during convalescence often give rise to states of stupor designated as mental confusion. The essential nature of these states is precisely the same as the symptoms of abulia and of mental disintegration taken to their extreme. The mechanism of this cerebral turbulence is not known; although the effect of toxins and poisons secreted by the microbes is suspected, still the facts have not been established. Is it not likely that these infectious diseases could in certain cases leave behind a less severe but longer stupor and that this poisoning could be the origin of the mental disintegration and indirectly of the fixed ideas? These comments are probably very true; by a strange coincidence, all the patients we have studied, as had Justine and Marcelle, had typhoid fever. Typhoid fever and other major infectious diseases must always be heeded in the antecedents to abulia and obsessiveness like syphilis as the antecedent to ataxia and general paralysis. Besides, observation of our patient has shown for sure that all the symptoms did not develop in a big way until after the typhoid fever and became even more pronounced later after a bout of influenza. The role of these infectious diseases is undeniable.

However, we do not believe this to be a complete explanation. First, because infectious diseases do not, in our opinion, have this effect in every individual, only in some whose antecedents create a marked predisposition. In the case before us, the obsession with cholera, the automatic speech, the double personality had definitely begun two years before the typhoid fever. The suggestibility, the tendency to fixed ideas, existed already in Justine's youth, and the study of this first phase of her life will prove for us the need to look back further than the typhoid fever at age nineteen, in order to uncover, if possible, the origin of the illness.

Justine was, in her early life, a prodigious child: very precocious in everything, astonishing in her wisdom and intelligence. No fits of temper or tears, an extremely gentle and lovable character, almost too reasonable even, at age five she was talking sensibly like a little woman. We are quite willing to accept these accounts, for at the hospital we have seen some of these utterly astonishing prodigious children. A little girl struck us most: at nine she was running the household and speaking sensibly of the worries she had about her older brother's behavior. At the same time she began the anorexia and the attacks of delirium that foreshadowed the end of this premature intelligence. The same happened to Justine: at six or seven something very important took place that, to our utmost regret, we cannot know about with sufficient precision. The child showed cerebral phenomena reminiscent of meningitis, first malaise and facial pallor, then violent headaches that provoked sharp cries, occasional convulsions, deviations in her eye movements, vomiting, stupor. But what is perplexing is that these accidents, which lasted only a couple of days at most, would be repeated nearly every week. It would be important to find out whether a rise in temperature accompanied these phenomena: Justine maintains that the doctor would note fever. The information is terribly vague. Is this a true encephalitic infection that paved the way for derangement, or was it rather already a hysterical pseudomeningitis following on earlier symptoms that had not been noticed?

These accidents recurred very frequently for several years, and at the same time there was a total change in her character. The child remained very intelligent, learning everything, but she was obstinate, given to emotionalism and to extreme anger. Some of her feelings were so exaggerated that they already seemed like fixed ideas and provoked frightful accidents; I will give just two examples. Justine was terrified of crawling animals, worms and snails, and had a tremendous passion for other animals, particularly cats. In order to cure these fears, the family doctor recommended a somewhat strange remedy: on his advice, during a walk, a big red snail was put on the then nine-year-old girl's neck. The impact was astonishing: Justine fell backward, unconscious and beset by spasms. It was difficult to bring her around and for several months she was absolutely obsessed by the memory of the snail; she would rub her neck as if she felt something there, and she would watch the hands of those around her to see whether they were hiding anything. Eight days after the attack, she had severe jaundice, which seemed to be connected to the emotions she had experienced.

The feeling, the passion for cats, gave rise to the second serious attack. Justine had a small cat that was accidentally injured: a hysterical attack and afterward a very curious outbreak of urticaria [hives]. Some time later, despite her protests, it was decided to put the wretched, sick cat to sleep. For Justine this led to incredible turmoil. Not only did she have convulsive attacks, followed by jaundice, but her body also changed totally, becoming so obese as to have difficulty in moving. At ten and a half she weighed 119 pounds. Here again we encounter a little known phenomenon that is very difficult to interpret on the basis of distant accounts. On different parts of her body, especially on those parts that stick out, on her temples, her breasts, her stomach, her calves, little spots appeared *symmetrically* on both sides of her body, then bluish patches; the skin became gangrenous; a small nearly painless wound opened up and did not fill in until later very slowly. Her menstruation, which began at about fourteen without problems, brought about another change: the obesity and the nutritional disturbances disappeared.

But at this point already, no doubt because of her mother's profession as a nurse, Justine was obsessed by the fear of death and illnesses. Migraines and even inexplicable bouts of delirium were provoked by this fixed idea that the young girl did not yet want to admit. The sight of the two people with cholera was the last straw for this already very shaken mind and determined the nature of the malady that was to take possession of her definitively.

It is very difficult to gather information about the patient's family; it took us a lot of effort and patience to put together the appended family tree, incomplete though it is. The information about her grandparents is wholly inadequate, and two individuals, R and S, have vanished or at least are unknown to the people I questioned. Notwithstanding these gaps, the tree strikes us as illuminating. Justine's father, A, an intelligent and industrious worker, had managed to establish a small business and to live in some ease. Unfortunately, he had been a drinker since his youth, and as he grew older, this vice assumed more and more the form of an illness. He would spend weeks and months without drinking, then following some emotion, especially grief, he would go out and drink for eight days on end. His death is irrelevant; he succumbed to smallpox; but is his drinking already the dipsomania we will see clearly in his children? It would be most interesting to know more precisely about his parents and whether they already had mental disturbances. We heard nothing specific about the grandfather C, but apparently the grandmother D was a woman of low intelligence and sordid slovenliness. So far mental illness evidently exists only embryonically in A and his parents. Unfortunately A marries a woman B of a similar disposition; from her father E she has extremely violent fits of rage; they were, it seems, absolutely identical in father and daughter. However, B somewhat complicated her father's rages, for she went so far as to lose consciousness and to end her rages in convulsions; the paternal vice clearly becomes a sickness in the daughter, and brutishness is complicated by hysteria. These original stains are on the whole quite low-grade, but they did not remain in isolation. The union of these two people, one alcoholic almost to the point of dipsomania, the other anger-ridden and hysterical, aggravated the situation enormously and brought about the family's ruin and death.

Let us look at these two people's descendants. At first glance, they are very numerous, for in half a century forty-six people have come from this initial couple. The great fecundity of the women in this family is remarkable; they each had ten to twelve children; this trait has been seen by some as a sign of degeneration. But fecundity depends on too many factors to allow us to emphasize this fact.

We are immediately surprised at the large number of children in this family who die at an early age, that is, before three, thirty-four children out of forty-six, that is, 74 percent (the average is below 20 percent); is this not a huge proportion, all the less explicable as we do not see in this family either excessive poverty, or major infectious diseases, or tuberculosis, or syphilis? How then did these children die? It is very difficult to know, and the symptoms can be indicated only vaguely. Obviously, among these thirty-four deaths, various infections, diarrhea, meningitis must be reckoned with. But we believe that infection played merely a secondary role here and we do not find ridiculous the common expression that Justine applied to her great-nephews: "They are hardly alive; they linger a year or two, skinny and pale, and they are extinguished like candles." What makes us believe that this mortality is due to hereditary vice is that it does not appear just once as an accident, but that it goes on increasing in each successive generation. In the descendants of A and B (the first generation on our tree), we count seven out of twelve children dying in early infancy, that is, 58 percent; in the following generation nineteen out of twenty-five, that is, 76 percent; and in the last generation eight out of nine, that is, 88 percent. If a fourth generation is born, which we do not think likely, it will foreseeably not live long.

Let us now consider the descendants of A and B who did survive. In the first generation, we see that all the living children suffer, to a greater or lesser extent, from the same malady as Justine; they all have disintegrating minds, tortured by impulsiveness and obsessions. Only the content of the obsession varies; K has fixed ideas of jealousy, blind and wild rages; J the impulse to drink. These impulses are now quite pathological: the unfortunate creature loses his conscience at the beginning of the bout, drinks all he can find, sleeps under bridges and by streams, and wakes up after eight days, confused and without memory; he dies of *delirium* [tremens]. Finally, L and M are also dipsomaniacs, but in addition they have drives to violence and even to murder.

Moving on to the second generation, we see the same familial traits, the obsessions and the violence in N, the dipsomania in O and T. But now we see new symptoms appearing; there are epileptics and idiots, O, Q, T, and in the last generation there is only one wretched epileptic boy, who will hardly reverse the family's decline. Its history is absolutely identical to those that served to establish Morel's theory of the final degeneration of a race. Unfortunately, the evolution is far from always being as fatal. It really seems as if families had illnesses just as individuals do, at times transient illnesses that strike only one or two generations, at other times serious illnesses that bring about the extinction of the race after several debilitated generations. In the case that we are studying, the two illnesses that were mild in the two original families combined to form a deadly illness.

This summary description has not taken us too far away from our patient because it seems to us that it becomes much easier to understand Justine when she is sited in her milieu. Her illness can no longer be attributed to some chance cause, to emotion or typhoid fever, when all her relations are brought into the picture, those who did not have the traumas but who present the same symptoms. It is likely that all the members of this family have the same psychological lesion; under the influence of heredity and alcoholic intoxication, the brain's superior functions, the functions of synthesizing current phenomena, diminish and disappear. Justine's cerebral state is one stage on this path that leads to the idiots who end the family, and it is not wrong to say that the origin of such an illness is mental degeneration.

This degeneration has taken a special form that can be found under other circumstances and that we have designated as the disintegration of the mind. Here a particular kind of psychological disintegration is involved. The poorly synthesized mental phenomena have the tendency to become manifest in two distinctive categories. We have noted the anesthesias, amnesias, subconscious acts, somnambulism, etc. The distinction is undoubtedly not always as absolutely apparent as in typical cases, but it is sufficiently pronounced. This mental disintegration takes the form of hysteria. In short we are dealing with a mental disintegration hereditary in origin and hysterical in form.

On the basis of this new information we can better assess the effects of our treatment. We are far from considering these hereditary illnesses as incurable and hopeless. The illnesses of a race can be cured like those of an individual, and in other genealogical tables we see the family recovering after being seriously affected for one or two generations. But at least we know that the illness reaches beyond the individual; that it has an extensive evolution and can hardly be changed by a few remedies briefly applied to one person. It is not credible that a patient like Justine could be cured completely of such an old and deep illness. After having described her tremendous and incontestable progress, it is necessary to note the remaining gaps and lesions in order to appreciate soberly the methods used.

The true sign of the cure of an illness is the departure of the doctor, who is sent away with pleasure; unfortunately, this sign does not

come in the patients with whom we are dealing; they are always incapable of sending their doctor away. All the progress we have
described in Justine's mental state is obtained and maintained only
by our continuous influence on her. This influence exerted by the
doctor on patients seems to us central in mental turbulence; it forms
a pathological characteristic in certain mental disorders. Without
here going into this phenomenon in general, let us merely recall how
Justine can manage to appear reasonable.

When Justine comes to see us, she is often in a pitiful state after
more or less serious attacks, obsessed by old fixed ideas that have
appeared again or new fixed ideas that have hit her. In the previous
days she has given up her usual work because she has not been capable of so much effort; she remains idle and uncomprehending; her
memory has gone, her sensitivity has diminished, her visual sense has
changed in a variety of ways. In the last resort, Justine feels *isolated,*
without support, and she yields to despair.

All these problems devolve in part from a very serious fact that cannot be overemphasized, the need for somnambulism. On the one
hand, somnambulism is analogous to her attacks and replaces them;
it seems as though the second existence must of necessity develop in
some form, and as one expression is forbidden to her, it surfaces in
another. On the other hand, these patients, so inclined to habit and
to automatism, have assumed the habit and consequently the intense
need to be put to sleep. This need, which should never be allowed to
arise without genuine medical necessity, seems to us quite as dangerous as the need for morphine, and it underlies in part the problems
we see in our patient on her arrival. But, we believe, there is still
another need that becomes apparent even in those patients of this
type who are not put to sleep, that is, the need to confess, to be scolded
and directed. This need is of an astonishing vehemence; it recurs to
the highest degree in all hysterics, neurasthenics, doubters, obsessives, etc.; in all individuals whose personal willpower is very weakened. Justine wants not only to be put to sleep; she wants to have suggestions made to her so that an outer authority dominates and rules
all the psychological phenomena she feels incapable of directing.

After the session using all the research and the methods described
above, some patients are immediately restored. This is what happens
to Justine: the struggle against the fixed ideas, the halting of the
attacks in their early stages have exhausted her, and despite all sorts
of measures she remains tired after the session. This malaise goes on
for half a day or a whole day and then the state of well-being sets in.

Justine no longer has fixed ideas; she feels energetic, capable of willpower and attention; she works regularly, studies attentively, and feels full of confidence: "I feel as if I had been given a tutor; I am no longer alone."

This feeling of "support" corresponds to very clear psychological facts that we cannot analyze here. The thought of the "director of conscience" persists in the minds of patients without their knowing it. I have tried to reproduce an English psychological experiment, "crystal-gazing," in a patient, Marguerite, during this phase of confiding that follows somnambulism. In this experiment subjects stare into a mirror or a glass globe and have visual hallucinations connected to their forgotten dreams and to their subconscious. When Marguerite would look into this globe on days following somnambulism, she would see my portrait; if, on the other hand, she looked in the same way a month later, in her days of "isolation" that preceded the somnambulism, she saw only the images from her dreams. This hallucination did not spring from her conscious thoughts, for in the second phase she wanted to see me again and thought of me much more than in the first phase. This latent influence is even stranger in Justine and is expressed spontaneously in hallucinations. Walking in the street, Justine finds herself before a hospital entrance, and, in keeping with her bad habit, she thinks of death, takes fright, and wants to make a big detour in order to avoid passing before its door. But there is an unexpected obstacle: she suddenly sees me in the middle of the road: "It was really you, just like now, you blocked my way; you forced me to pass right in front of the door, and when the door had been crossed, you began to laugh, and I don't know where you were." At other times she has auditory hallucinations; she hears me reproaching her, and she hears it so loudly that she turns around to ask whether I am there. She engages in most extraordinary conversations with me; she asks my advice, and it seems that I respond very well. The strangest thing is that this advice is not always a repetition of what I told her in somnambulism. There are new questions that I have never addressed: fortunately she ascribes to me only very wise words. Such direction, even if it results in apparent health, is still a peculiarly pathological fact.

Unquestionably Justine succeeds by means of intellectual work in increasing her power of attention and in better synthesizing phenomena, but this result is obtained only at the cost of an enormous, continuous effort. To make a comparison, she is constantly in the state we ourselves are in when we have to prepare for a competition or to compose a complicated paper. For practical life, for banal perceptions, she needs as much effort as ordinary people do for an original, difficult piece of work. So it is quite natural that she grows tired and discouraged: "I know that if I stop working I will become deranged, but it's so tiring that I can't keep at it!" The automatic phenomena hit her again: the need for direction and encouragement is again just as strong, and Justine has to go back to the doctor.

This continual need for direction can take very many different forms such as hysterics' need for somnambulism, the desire for extraneous affirmation on the part of doubters, or simply the need for affection, the fear of solitude, etc. Studying her is most interesting for it allows us to enter in an almost experimental manner into the analysis of moral feelings, yet nonetheless it presents great difficulties in mental therapeutics. In certain cases, any therapy of this kind is quite impossible. Many patients we have known can theoretically be cured, but they require devotion and continual strengthening at least once a day. Such sessions are tiring, they are not always interesting, and above all they take a very long time. Such treatments are practically impossible.

Having sought to assume direction of a patient's mind, we come to a new problem, that of reducing this direction to the necessary minimum, that is to say, to space out the sessions. Rarely is this problem completely resolved; we can list only a small number of patients whom we have been able to leave completely to their own devices. With some, as with Justine in particular, the problem is partly resolved when the sessions with the patient can be spaced out more.

At the beginning, I had to see Justine very frequently, several times a week; then for long once a week sufficed. We managed, not without difficulty, to grant the patient only one confession per month, and in the past year she has stood this well. We have not been able to go further: recently, after trying to space out the sessions to six weeks, we had some bad symptoms appear again. However, we must acknowledge that at one month's interval Justine's sessions are not too numerous. How many patients with organic afflictions or infirmities need a surgeon or a doctor every month! But it is nevertheless true that this person, on account of her hereditary cerebral weakness, does not recover completely; she remains enfeebled. Our excellent teacher, Dr. Jules Falret, told us an anecdote that used to be little understood and on which my studies seem to shed light. The great alienist of Rouen, Morel, had undertaken the treatment of a deranged woman by the procedures of animal magnetism. He succeeded magnificently and could get the patient out of the madhouse, but she would go back very frequently and he was not dissatisfied with these repeated visits, which allowed him to note the good effects of his care. Morel died, and two weeks later, the patient, totally delirious, had to be committed to the hospital again, this time permanently. We hope that nothing of the sort will happen to our patients, but we fully realize that if for one reason or another they were abandoned, they would very quickly relapse. This limitation of the therapeutic effect, this powerlessness on our part to transform our patients' thoughts once and for all, confirms our studies of the origins of the illness. The hereditary lesion is too deep, it was formed over several generations, it cannot be repaired other than slowly through new generations; in the course of an individual life, it can be more or less palliated but not cured.

It is futile to dwell on these general comments, which would hardly be justified by the study of one patient: we wanted only to engage in observation. She let us confirm previous comments on hysterical phenomena and especially on abulia. She has shown us some new, not unimportant details on fixed ideas and their treatment. It may also hold some interest for psychology: the nature of certain ideas, their organization, their disintegration, their reduction to partial and incomplete phenomena seem to us applicable to the interpretation of the healthy as well as of the sick mind. Pedagogy and morality must take an interest in these facts, which show the power of intellectual work, the progress of attention, the need for sympathy and for direction. It is in bringing together observations of this kind that we will come to understand the sick as well as the apparently healthy mind a little better.

Bibliography

Primary Sources

Beard, George M. *American Nervousness*. 1883. Reprint, New York: Arno Press, 1972.

———. "Neurasthenia, or Nervous Exhaustion." *Boston Medical and Surgical Journal* 3: no. 13 (29 April 1869): 219–21.

———. *Practical Treatise on Nervous Exhaustion*. 1881. Reprint, New York: Arno Press, 1971.

Bernheim, Hippolyte. *Hypnosis and Suggestion in Psychotherapy: A Treatise on the Nature and Uses of Hypnotism*. Translated by Christian A. Herter. New York: Jason Aronson, 1973.

———. *New Studies in Hypnotism*. Translated by Richard S. Sandor. New York: International Universities Press, 1980.

Braid, James. *Neurypnology*. 1843. Reprint, New York: Arno Press, 1976.

Briquet, Pierre. *Traité clinique et thérapeutique de l'hystérie*. Paris: Baillère, 1859.

Charcot, Jean-Martin. *Comptes rendus hebdomadaires des séances de l'Académie des sciences,* 94 (Janvier-Juin 1882). Paris: Gauthier-Villars, 1882. Reprint, Nendeln, Liechtenstein: Kraus, 1978.

———. *Leçons du mardi 1887–88*. Translated by Christopher G. Goetz. New York: Raven Press 1987.

———. *Leçons sur les maladies du système nerveux faites à la Salpêtrière*. 3rd ed. Paris: Delahaye, 1877; *Clinical Lectures on Diseases of the Nervous System*. London: New Sydenham Society, 1877.

———. *A Propos d'un cas d'hystérie masculine. Oeuvres complètes*. Vol. 9, Paris: Delahaye & Lecrosière, 1888–94.

Freud, Sigmund. "An Analysis of a Case of Hysteria." In *Standard Edition of the Complete Psychological Works of Sigmund Freud*, edited by James Strachey. Vol. 7, 1–122. Reprint, London: Hogarth Press, 1953–74.

———. *Bruchstück einer Hysterie-Analyse*. In *Gesammelte Werke*. Vol. 5, 161–286. (1904–5). London: Imago, 1942.

———. *Complete Letters*. Edited and translated by Jeffrey M. Masson. Cambridge: Harvard Univ. Press, 1985.

———. *Studien über Hysterie*. [*Studies on Hysteria*]. In *Gesammelte Werke*. Vol. 1, 75–251. (1892–95). London: Imago, 1942.

Janet, Pierre. "Les actes inconscients de la mémoire pendant le somnambulisme." *Revue philosophique* 25, no. 1 (1888): 238–79.

———. "Étude sur un cas d'aboulie et d'idées fixes." *Revue philosophique* 31, no. 1 (1891): 258–87, 382–407.

———. "Étude sur un cas d'amnésie antérograde dans la maladie de la désagrégation psychologique." In *International Congress of Experimental Psychology*, 26–30. London: Williams & Norgate, 1982.

———. "Histoire d'une idée fixe." *Revue philosophique* 37, (1894): 121–68.

———. "L'amnésie et la dissociation des souvenirs." *Journal de Psychologie* 1 (1904): 28–37.

———. "Un cas de délire systématisé dans la paralysie générale." *Journal de Psychologie* 3 (1906): 329–33.

Krafft-Ebing, Richard. *Psychopathia Sexualis.* 3rd. ed., Translated by F. B. Rebman. Brookly, NY: Physicians and Surgeons Book Company, 1926.

Liébeault, Ambroise-Auguste. *Le Sommeil provoqué et les états analogues.* 1889. Reprint, New York: Arno Press, 1976.

Schnitzler, Arthur. "Über funktionelle Aphonie und deren Behandlung durch Hypnose und Suggestion." In *Medizinische Schriften,* edited by Horst Thomé, 176–209. Wien and Darmstadt: Paul Zsolnay Verlag, 1988.

Tuke, Daniel Hack. *Illustrations of the Influence of the Mind upon the Body in Health and Disease.* Philadelphia: Lea's Sons, 1884.

SECONDARY SOURCES

Abse, D. Wilfred. *Hysteria and Related Mental Disorders.* Bristol: Wright, 1987.

Ackerknecht, Erwin H. *A Short History of Medicine.* Baltimore and London: The Johns Hopkins UP, (1955) 1982.

Beizer, Janet. *Ventriquolized Bodies.* Ithaca, N.Y., and London: Cornell UP, 1994.

Bronfen, Elisabeth. *The Knotted Subject: Hysteria and its Discontents.* Princeton, N.J.: Princeton University Press, 1998.

Buranelli, Vincent. *The Wizard from Vienna.* New York: Coward, McCann & Geoghan, 1975.

Certeau, Michel de. "The Freudian Novel: History and Literature." *Humanities and Society* 4, nos. 2 and 3 (1981): 121–41.

Chertok, Leon, and Raymond de Saussure. *The Therapeutic Revolution from Mesmer to Freud.* Translated by R. H. Ahrenfeldt. New York: Brunner & Mazel, 1979.

Cohn, Dorrit. "Freud's Case Histories and the Question of Fictionality." In *Telling Facts: History and Facts in Psychoanalysis,* edited by Joseph Smith and Humphrey Morris, 21–47. Baltimore and London: The Johns Hopkins University Press, 1992.

Dowbiggin, Ian. "Degeneration and Hereditarianism." In *Madhouses, Mad-Doctors and Madmen: The Social History of Psychiatry in the Victorian Era,* 188–232. Philadelphia: University of Pennsylvania Press, 1981.

Drinka, George F. *The Birth of Neurosis: Myth, Malady and the Victorians.* New York: Simon & Schuster, 1984.

Ellenberger, Henri. *The Discovery of the Uniconscious.* New York: Basic Books, 1970.

Erb, Wilhelm. *Handbuch der Elektrotherapie.* Leipzig: Verlag von F. C. W. Vogel, 1882.

Ey, Henri. "History and Analysis of the Concept of Hysteria." *La Revue du practicien* 14 (1964): 1417–34. Reprint, in *Hysteria* edited by Alec Roy, 1–16. New York: John Wiley & Sons, 1982.

Furst, Lillian R. "Anxious Doctor/Anxious Patients." *LIT* 8 (1997): 259–77.

———. "Girls for Sale: Freud's Dora and Schnitzler's Else." *Modern Austrian Literature* 34: 3/4 (2003): 80–02.

———. *Idioms of Distress.* Albany: State University Press of New York, 2003.

Gamwell, Lynn and Nancy Tooms. *Madness in America: Cultural and Medical Perceptions of Illness before 1914.* Ithaca and London: Cornell University Press, 1995.

Goldstein, Jan. *Console and Classify: The French Psychiatric Profession in the Nineteenth Century.* Chicago: University of Chicago Press (1987) 2001.

Gosling, F. G. *Before Freud: Neurasthenia and the American Medical Community 1970– 1910.* Urbana and Chicago: University of Illinois Press, 1987.

Greenway, John L. " 'Nervous Disease' and Electrical Medicine." In *Pseudo-Science and Society in Nineteenth-Century America,* edited by Arthur Wrobelin, 46–73. Lexington: University of Kentucky Press, 1987.

Herzog, Hilary H. " 'Medizin ist eine Weltanschauung': On Schnitzler's Medical Writings." In *A Companion to the Works of Arthur Schnitzler,* edited by Dagmar C. Lorenz, 227–41. Rochester, N.Y.: Camden House, 2003.

Lunbeck, Elizabeth. *The Psychiatric Persuasion: Knowledge, Gender, and Power in Modern America.* Princeton, N.J.: Princeton University Press, 1994.

Micale, Mark S. and Paul Lerner, eds. *Traumatic Pasts: History, Psychiatry, and Trauma in the Modern Age.* Cambridge: Cambridge University Press, 2001.

Oppenheim, Janet. *"Shattered Nerves": Doctors, Patients, and Depression in Victorian England.* New York: Oxford University Press, 1991.

Rosenberg, Charles E. "The Bitter Fruit: Heredity, Disease, and Social Thought." In *No Other Gods: On Science and American Social Thought,* 25–53. Baltimore, The Johns Hopkins University Press, 1976.

———. "Body and Mind in Nineteenth-Century Medicine." In *Explaining Epidemics and Other Studies in the History of Medicine,* 74–89. New York: Cambridge University Press, 1992.

———. "The Place of George M. Beard in Nineteenth-Century Psychiatry." *Bulletin of the History of Medicine* 36 (1962): 245–59.

Scull, Andrew (ed.). *Madhouses, Mad-Doctors, and Madmen: The Social History of Psychiatry in the Victorian Era.* Philadelphia: University of Pennsylvania Press, 1981.

Shorter, Edward. *A History of Psychiatry from the Age of the Asylum to the Age of Prozac.* New York: Wiley, 1997.

Slavney, Phillip R. *Perspectives on "Hysteria."* Baltimore: The Johns Hopkins University Press, 1990.

Tatar, Maria. *Spellbound: Studies in Mesmerism and Literature.* Princeton, N.J.: Princeton University Press, 1978.

Trillat, Etienne. *Histoire de l'hystérie.* Paris: Seghers, 1986.

Veith, Ilza. *Hysteria: The History of a Disease.* Chicago & London: University of Chicago Press, 1970.

Waterfield, Robin. *Hidden Depths: The Story of Hypnosis.* New York: Brunner-Routledge, 2003.

Winter, Alison. *Mesmerized: Powers of Mind in Victorian Britain.* Chicago & London: University of Chicago Press, 1998.